Asking
for Trouble **1**

SHERRYL CLARK

Illustrated by Kristin Headlam

sundance™
A Haights Cross Communications ® Company

A Haights Cross Communications ✦® Company

Published by
Sundance Publishing
P.O. Box 740
One Beeman Road
Northborough, MA 01532
800-343-8204

First published 1999 as Supa Dazzlers by
Addison Wesley Longman Australia Pty Limited
95 Coventry Street
South Melbourne 3205 Australia
Exclusive United States Distribution: Sundance Publishing

ISBN-13: 978-0-7608-4801-2
ISBN-10: 0-7608-4801-7

Printed in China

Contents

Chapter 1

Moving to the Country

"I know what you're like, Leo Marrelli. You stay out of trouble while I'm at work."

"Yes, Mom." I slid further down on the couch and clicked the remote control again. Five channels—boring, boring, boring. There was nothing to do, nowhere to go. It was all right for her, driving her dumb taxi all over the countryside.

"I'm not putting up with any more of your tricks," she had said. "Vacations spell nothing but trouble. You go out with those friends of yours and the next thing I know, I'm down at the police station again."

Again! It was only twice, and it wasn't my fault either time. Nick lifted a CD from a store, and we all got blamed. And those jerks from the private school started that fight down at the park.

Everything was always my fault. She packed up all our stuff and moved us to this hick town that was so small it didn't even have a video arcade. Now, she was driving the town's only taxi, which I didn't tell any of my friends because it was so embarrassing. *And* she brought us here at the beginning of summer vacation, saying it was to keep me out of trouble. Ha! I'd show her.

I went outside to get my bike out of the shed in our overgrown backyard.

"Where are you going?"

"Mind your own business!"

"Mom didn't say you could go out." Julie, my little sister, stood in the doorway, hands on her hips. She was doing her Mom impression.

"She didn't say I couldn't, either."

"I'll tell."

"Big deal, do what you like." I coasted my bike down the rough driveway and out onto the street. "Go write a letter about it!" I yelled as I pedaled away. Since we'd been here—a whole three days—Julie had written about twenty letters to her friends back in the city.

She was sure they would never forget
her, and they were all coming to visit. I'd
rather die than have my friends see me in
this dump.

I rode around the corner, down to the end of
Main Street, and back. Then I did it again.
Eight stores, a cafe, and a gas station. I was
going to go crazy.

I set off in the opposite direction, following the sign to the football field. In three minutes, I'd passed it, a patch of dead grass with skinny posts at each end. It didn't look as if a game had been played there for years. I was out of town now, no houses in sight—just fields and trees. I kept going.

The first big hill had me puffing. I hopped off at the top and listened. Magpies warbled, crows screeched, and a few other birds chirped. And I could hear kids' voices, too, off to my left. I peered through the scrubby trees and saw a path. That's where they must be.

I rode slowly along the path and stopped when the voices sounded close. Then I snuck up to where I could see them. The path widened into a huge clearing where a mountain of gravel stood.

The gravel must have been dumped there
by the highway department. Half a dozen
boys and two girls were riding up and over
and around the gravel mountain on a
crisscross of trails.

At last I had found some action. I pushed my
bike into the open, then rode to the edge of
the gravel. One by one, the others saw me
and stopped. On top of the mountain, a tall,
red-haired boy stood glaring down at me.

"What do you want, city slicker?"

"Just passing by."

"Keep going then."

"It's a free country."

"This is our hill. We don't want troublemakers messing it up," the tall boy said.

"Yeah, my mom told me about you," a girl added.

Great—they knew my life story already. My face got hot, and I gripped the handlebars. "Couldn't get into trouble on that puny little hill. That's nothing to what I'm used to."

They all looked at the tall boy, who just stared down at me and sneered, "Yeah? Prove it."

Chapter 2

King of the Mountain

I smiled, remembering the railway embankments and old slag heaps I'd conquered with my buddy, Tron. I pushed off, worked up some speed and took the first rise, lifting my front wheel, then pedaled hard up the next slope to the top. I could see where the others had been, and I stuck to the flattened trails at first. Then I started to dip into the loose gravel on the down slopes, spraying it off the back wheel and sliding around. My audience watched silently.

After a few minutes of hard riding, I got to the top and stopped next to the tall boy. "Told you it was easy," I said, trying not to breathe too hard.

"Of course it's easy," said the boy. "We're only messing around. If you want a real ride, smart guy, try Hollows Bridge. Then we might let you ride with us." He jerked his head at the others. "Come on, let's get away from the bad smell around here."

The others snickered and rode off behind the tall boy, leaving me alone again.

"What a pack of amateurs," I muttered. "I probably made them look bad." But whether that was true or not, I was alone again. I headed back into town, wondering what and where Hollows Bridge was. It was lunchtime, my stomach said, and I got home just as Mom pulled into the driveway.

Her red bomber would have been OK if it wasn't plastered with TAXI and phone number signs.

"Where have you been?" Mom demanded.

"Just riding around."

"Hmmm," she said, and went inside.

Lunch was sandwiches as usual. "We'll have some Morty's potpies for dinner," said Mom. "They're the best ever. You'll love them. I used to eat them all the time when I was a kid."

That was the trouble. Mom had lived in this dump when she was little. She was living in a dreamworld now, thinking it was the perfect place to bring up kids. She just couldn't see how boring it was. She probably spent all her time here making dolls' clothes and baking cookies.

If I went back to the city, I could stay with Tron. Mom could pay Tron's parents some money for room and board, and I could go back to my old school. Tron and I had worked it all out, but Mom had just said no. She wouldn't even listen. It wasn't fair.

The phone rang, and Mom answered it in her stuffy work voice. "Yes, Mrs. Row, I'll be there in a few minutes. No trouble at all." She grabbed her sandwich and gulped down the rest of her iced tea. "Got to go, kids. It's another job."

It was all right for her.

"What's up, grouch?" Julie grinned at me across the table.

"What are you so happy about? Written your hundredth letter to your stupid friends?"

"At least my friends will write back," she said. "None of yours *can* write."

"Very funny. Just you wait. In another month, they'll all forget you."

"No, they won't. They've got brains and memories, not like your friends."

"Yeah, right." I couldn't be bothered keeping it up. I went into the living room to find the TV page in the newspaper. Nothing worth watching. I felt like kicking the TV.

Julie yelled, "I'm going to mail my letters. You want anything from the store?"

"Nah."

I sat on the couch and tried to imagine what Tron and Tony and Nick would be doing right now. Playing video games, or riding around the mall parking lot, or going to the movies if they had any money. I thought about the gravel hill—I could ride over it again . . . but it was no fun on my own. If Tron were here, we'd make it really dangerous. We'd ride headfirst down all the slippery parts. Those kids I saw were probably all chicken. They'd never try anything like that.

Julie burst in through the front door. "Hey, the kids here have a go-cart. They're riding it down the big hill by the dump."

"Big deal."

"Well, I'm going," said Julie. "I met this girl named Lisa at the store. We're going to watch. She said Kenny gives her a ride sometimes, and I might get one, too."

"Kenny who?"

"I don't know. You can stay here and be a pain if you want. I'm going." And she was off.

I just knew that the tall, red-haired boy was Kenny, the Boss—the big star of this stupid hole. I looked around and stared at the little black spots in the carpet near the fireplace where sparks had jumped out. Maybe the house would burn down. Then we could all go back to the city.

Another minute of staring around the room was all I could take. Before I could stop myself, I was out the door and walking toward the dump.

Chapter 3

The Big Slide Down

1, 2, 3, GO !

Why am I doing this? They'll only ignore me.

At least it was something to do. Anything was better than absolutely nothing.

Past the gas station, the road rose up a little, then rose up more sharply again before heading down into a valley that was like a pit. I'd never actually seen a real go-cart. I had only heard about them. Just as I reached the bottom of the first hill, a four-wheeled rocket zoomed past me and came to a stop a hundred feet away. A pink-faced kid jumped out, pulled the cart around by its steering rope, and began to drag it back up the hill.

"This is the worst part," he puffed as he passed me. "You've got to take it back up for the next kid."

Someone had spoken to me! I followed him and hesitated on the first rise. At the top of the second rise, a group of kids were milling around. Some were waiting for the go-cart, some were pushing on a sheet of tin. I could see the red-haired boy and Julie, who waved wildly when she saw me . . . another embarrassing family member. I thought about whether to turn and go home or continue on. I'd look pathetic if I left now, so I kept walking. But everyone just ignored me. I stood back near the bank to watch.

Someone else set off in the cart, whooping and yelling. It looked like a real blast, but I was more interested in the tin sheet. They'd bent the front up into a curve and tied a piece of rope through two holes for a handle. Now they were ready to ride the sheet down the hill on the slippery grass.

"You go, Jamie, it's your tin."

The tall boy looked straight across at me. "I say *he* goes first."

"No way, Kenny, it's my tin," Jamie protested.

"You game, Slicker? Too easy for you?" Kenny grinned. My stomach clenched as I sized up the tin with its sharp, ragged edges.

If I fell off, I could end up with a slice out of me that no bandage could ever fix. But that was better than being called a chicken.

I shrugged. "Nothing hard about that," I said. I walked forward. In the silence, all I could hear was the cart being dragged up the hill. I sat on the old sack that folded over the back edge for pushing. When I gripped the rope and looked down, the hill seemed like a cliff.

"Give him a good, hard shove," said Kenny.

Before I could say "Ready," the tin sheet jumped forward with a tremendous lurch. I was off, sliding and bumping over the grass. The rope was useless for steering. Only the bank rising on my right helped keep the tin roughly on course. I wanted to close my eyes, but instead I braced my legs and hung on. Halfway down the hill, the tin began to slow. When it hit a patch of bare dirt, it jerked sideways and stopped. I dropped the rope and willed the shaking inside me to stop. Then I stood up. Jamie pounded down the hill behind me.

"See?" he said. "You don't know how to do it. I told Kenny you wouldn't." He took the rope and began to drag the tin back up the hill. "Told you," he yelled.

"All right," said Kenny, "who else wants to try it?" I saw Julie open her mouth to volunteer, and I glared at her.

"It's my tin and my turn," Jamie said.

Kenny eyed him. "I suppose so—just be careful."

"I can make it go better than he did," said Jamie. He sat on the sack, braced his legs, and took hold of the rope. "Push it *hard* this time."

The two boys at the back chanted, "One, two, three, *go!*" and shoved. At first the tin moved smoothly—then it seemed to hit a bump. It twisted around and hit the bank, throwing Jamie off. We waited, but he didn't get up. He just lay there, holding his arm.

Chapter 4

Who's  Chicken?

Kenny ran down and knelt next to Jamie. Then he called, "Lisa, go home and get Mom's first-aid kit, the one with the big bandage in it. Hurry!" A small blonde girl took off at top speed, her hair flying in the wind. The others stood around as Kenny held Jamie's arm tightly. We could see blood seeping between his fingers—lots of it.

One of the boys turned to me. "It's your fault. You must have bent it." I just gaped at him. I didn't do anything!

"Don't be stupid, Ben!" Kenny snapped.

"He's a show-off. Tell him to go home."

"Yeah," said the girl from that morning. "He's trouble."

"And he's chicken," said another boy. "Look at him shaking in his boots. He thinks we're going to beat him up."

My fingers curled into fists. If only Tron or Tony or Nick were here now. They'd show this bunch of losers. I was no chicken—no way. I was ready for the first punch.

Just then Lisa arrived back with the first-aid kit. She puffed as she pulled out antiseptic and bandages from the white box. "Put it

on here," Kenny instructed. He let his fingers
part to reveal a jagged gash in Jamie's arm.
Jamie looked so pale I thought he might
pass out. Lisa dribbled the antiseptic
carefully along the wound.

"Now put on a piece of that stuff." He
pointed at a long strip of cloth bandage. It
turned red only a few seconds after Lisa put
it on. "Hold it on," Kenny said. Lisa kept it

steady, while Kenny wrapped a thicker
bandage around Jamie's arm as tightly and
carefully as he could.

"We better get him home fast," Kenny said.

"What about the city slicker?" Ben asked.
"Are you going to fix him?"

All eyes turned to me. I gritted my teeth and stared right back at them.

"Hollows Bridge," Kenny said. "Ten, tomorrow morning."

"Yeah, that'll prove he's chicken," Ben said, and they all moved off, leaving Julie and me alone with the piece of tin.

"You've done it again, haven't you?" she said. "You'll be dead if Mom finds out."

I didn't reply. I was too busy wondering what Hollows Bridge was. And I had a horrible feeling it wasn't good.

At dinner that night, while Mom raved over every mouthful of her Morty's potpie, I tried to force some down my throat.

"Come on, Leo," Mom said. "Morty's potpies are much better than those frozen supermarket ones." Then she got that suspicious glint in her eyes. "You're not in trouble again, are you? You weren't involved when that Johnson boy cut his arm, were you? He had to have nine stitches."

"No, of course not," I muttered, jabbing my potpie. I remembered how Jamie hadn't made a sound, hadn't cried or anything. That was pretty tough. "How come everyone knows everyone's business around here?"

"That's how a small town is," Mom said. "You'll appreciate it one day."

Not likely.

After dinner, I had to help Julie with the dishes. "Are you going to Hollows Bridge tomorrow?" she whispered.

"I suppose I'll have to, except I don't know where it is."

"It's up a side road past the dump. It's really old and rotten."

"How do you know?"

"Lisa told me." She grinned at me. "She's my new friend."

"Kenny's sister? You must be desperate."

"At least I've got a friend instead of twelve enemies," she hissed.

Chapter 5

Bridge of Doom

I didn't sleep well, tossing and turning, and dreaming of being buried under gravel. I woke up when Mom called, "I'm going now. I have a job. Stay out of trouble, Leo."

"Yeah, yeah. Give me a break." I lay back and sighed. Hollows Bridge . . . I was doomed. By 9:45, I was wheeling out my bike, wishing I was anywhere but here. Even detention would be better. Julie rode up next to me.

"Are you sure you want to do this?" she asked. "Lisa said—"

"Stuff Lisa."

"But you have to ride across Hollows Bridge."

"So? It's only a bridge."

"It's got big holes in it. It's rotten."

"It can't be that bad or no one would get across it."

"But—"

"Shut up, will you? I'll show these kids what a pack of deadheads they are, and that'll be it."

I shoved off and pedaled hard, trying to leave her behind . . . but each time I looked back, she was still there. Oh, well, bad luck

for her. I passed yesterday's hill, the dump,
and the faded sign that read, "Hollows Road."
The gravel road was overgrown with bushes
and weeds, and halfway up the hill, I had to
get off my bike and wheel it to the top. There
I found Kenny, Ben, Lisa, and more than a
dozen other kids, waiting. Every kid in town
had come out of his or her rabbit hole to
watch.

"Chicken's here," Ben crowed, "and this will
prove it."

What was with this kid? It was like he knew I'd lose before I even started. Well, I'd show them. Leo Marrelli had done a lot of tough stuff. They'd be sorry.

"Cut it out, Ben," said Kenny. He turned to me and pointed down into the gully. "That's Hollows Bridge. All you have to do is ride down this hill and cross the bridge."

"Is that all?" They had to be kidding. The hill wasn't that steep, and the bridge looked OK. I swung my leg over my bike and settled on the seat. "I'm no chicken, and I'll prove it," I said, and pushed off. I heard Julie yell, "Leo!" but I didn't look back.

As I gathered speed, I was tempted to brake a little and get a better look at the bridge. But what did it matter? I had to cross it now, no matter what. Then I began to see the condition of the old wooden structure. I could see that the dark stripes on it were missing planks—more gaps than planks, some big enough to swallow my whole bike!

There might be a path across, if I went fast enough and stayed on the right where the planks looked closer together. No, this was crazy. I'd die or break something, for sure. I began to slow down. There was still time to stop. Then I heard yelling behind me. I looked over my shoulder and saw them all running down the hill after me. If I stopped now, I'd be the biggest joke ever. No one laughed at Leo Marrelli. I'd rather die.

Chapter 6

Hanging Out

I sped up again, focusing on the right side of the bridge. I could do it. I'd show them.

And I almost made it. Three-quarters of the way across, my front wheel caught in a hole I hadn't seen. Almost in slow motion, I felt myself leave the seat, catapulting through the air and landing on the old railing. The railing gave way with an enormous crack, but at the last minute, I grabbed an upright post.

Miraculously the post held. But I was suspended in midair, dangling above a patch of blackberries and a bunch of jagged rocks. All I could do was hang on. I didn't dare swing my legs up, in case the post broke.

Everyone had stopped at the other end of the bridge.

"Let him fall," said Ben.

"Shut up, will you?" snapped Kenny. "You're a real jerk sometimes." He shouted to me, "Can you get up?"

"No, the post's going to give," I yelled back.

"Help him, you idiots!" That was Julie, embarrassing me as usual. My arms ached, and I was sure the post had groaned.

Someone was picking his way across the

bridge, stepping around the holes. It was Kenny, his face looked serious as he concentrated on where to step next. When he reached me, he crouched down.

"If you let one hand go, I can pull you up."

"Why would you help me?" I could see myself on the rocks, while Kenny laughed, victoriously.

"Why not? You won the dare. Fair's fair."

"I didn't win. I didn't get across."

"No one else has had the guts to even try."

"You mean—" I couldn't finish. No one had even tried before? And I was the idiot who got suckered into it.

"Give me your hand." Kenny braced his feet and held out his hand. I reached up and

grabbed it, and in a few seconds I was safely back on the bridge.

"Thanks," I said, sitting up and taking a deep breath. I looked around for my bike. It lay on its side. The front wheel was buckled.

"You must've hit that hole pretty hard."

"Yeah, I wasn't expecting it. It wrecked my wheel. Mom will kill me."

"It's not that bad," Kenny said. "Dad's got a vice in the shed. He'll help us fix it, but we'd better get off this bridge before the whole thing goes." He got up, then went to pick up my bike.

Kenny's too bossy to ever be a real friend, I thought, but we carried the bike off the bridge together and set out for home.

About the Author

Sherryl Clark

Sherryl Clark has been writing stories, poems, and plays for nearly twenty years. Her first children's book was called *The Too-Tight Tutu*. She teaches writing and editing classes, and also helps people to publish their own books.

Sherryl lives with her husband and her daughter, two cats, and six chickens.

About the Illustrator

Kristin Headlam

Kristin Headlam is a painter and printmaker, who lives with her dog, Dora Pamphlet. She has regular exhibitions of her work.

To supplement the income of a starving artist, Kristin teaches painting and illustrates books.

Kristin says she will try anything that comes along, as long as she gets to keep painting.

WOMEN WHO WIN

Women Athletes on Being the Best

Lisa Taggart

SEAL PRESS

Women Who Win
Women Athletes on Being the Best

Copyright © 2007 Lisa Taggart

Published by Seal Press
1400 65th Street, Suite 250
Emeryville, CA 94608

Library of Congress Cataloging-in-Publication Data

Taggart, Lisa.
Women who win : women athletes on being the best / Lisa Taggart.
p. cm.
Includes bibliographical references and index.
ISBN-13: 978-1-58005-200-9 (alk. paper)
ISBN-10: 1-58005-200-2 (alk. paper)
1. Women athletes-United States-Biography. I. Title.

GV697.A1T34 2007
796'.0820922-dc22
[B]
2007003955

Cover design by Gerilyn Attebery
Interior design by Tabitha Lahr
Printed in the U.S.A.

To Jimbo, a true rock-star jock-star, who plays like a champion and is always a good sport

Contents

Introduction

Writing this book changed the way I look at the world. After studying the stories of the ten incredible women in these pages, more than I'd imagined seems possible.

In these pages, ten champions describe their inspirations and their struggles. Here are the tales of ten leaders who broke barriers and records: four Olympians and seven world champions. No one told these women exactly how to become the best in the world; each had to find her own path and face her own unexpected challenges.

Before I started out, I already had some knowledge of the accomplishments of these athletes; I'd heard the name Lynn Hill many times (spoken in hushed, awed tones), particularly when traveling in rock-climbing areas like Yosemite National Park and Boulder, Colorado. And marathoner Deena Kastor is revered in my circle of friends, which includes many runners; they usually simply shake their heads and murmur "wow" when her name comes up.

But it wasn't until I heard the details of Karen Smyers's struggles with injury and illness, doing the math to figure out that she competed in the Olympic triathlon trials four months after surgery for thyroid cancer and five months after breaking her collarbone, that I really grasped the level of dedication required of world-class athletes. I'd known there was a woman out there who'd broken all kinds of barriers in horse racing, but it wasn't until I learned of Julie Krone's fistfights with fellow jockeys, her illicit entry onto the track at Churchill Downs to get her first job, and her multiple comebacks after injury, trauma, and retirement, that I understood just how scrappy a pioneer female jockey had to be to get her seat in the saddle. And Julie Foudy's contributions to the sport of soccer were evident to anyone watching the U.S. national team play in the World Cup and the Olympics, but it turns out that her contributions to the sport off the field are just as great, and continue to grow.

Learning these stories, I thought that if these women could work so hard and triumph over so many obstacles, then maybe I could be a little bit stronger, a little bit tougher, a little bit better in the way I approach things. I'd made a habit while writing this book of taking daily (more or less) breaks for a modest jog/plod around my neighborhood. But after interviewing Deena Kastor, I found myself pushing the pace. I always stopped at the local coffee shop for a mocha as a post-run reward. One day as I was slowing down at Mission City Coffee Roasters, a voice in my head asked, *What would Deena do?* I ran all the way home.

Later that week, during a meeting at work, a coworker of mine misstated important details in a project, overlooking one contributor. Like many writers, I usually have a hard time speaking up, particularly in large, formal group settings like the one I was in. But I thought, *What would Julie do?* And so I cleared my throat and pointed out the problem; I know the overlooked employee appreciated it.

We like hearing about champions because their stories encourage us to stretch ourselves. Because they widen our view of the possible. And they expand our dreams. If someone else has climbed so high or run so fast, then maybe we could try to go a little bit farther ourselves. Gold does rub off. "I was a better human being when I was with that team," the coach for the 1999 women's World Cup soccer team, Tony DiCicco, told me, the nostalgia in his voice transmitting through the telephone wires. "Everyone owed their success to the team. That was part of the culture."

There's the old saying that if you want to soar with the eagles, you have to go where the eagles soar. These women know exactly where that is. They can inspire you to fly, too.

It's astonishing to think that only thirty-six years ago, women were not allowed—not *allowed*—to run the Boston marathon. That only twenty-four years ago, rhythmic gymnast Wendy Hilliard was told she couldn't represent the United States on the national team because a coach thought the color of her skin meant she didn't fit in. And it's shocking to think that more recently—only four years ago—federal administrators were considering drastically weakening the tenets of Title IX, the 1972 legislation that opened the door to equal sports opportunities for girls and women.

Women need sports. Girls need sports. We all need to explore the limits of our power, push our strength, find something that drives us to keep going beyond pain and fatigue, beyond what others have identified as the edge of our abilities. We're more capable wherever we go after we've figured out how to play with a team, and with different teams, and when we've learned how to compete well—passionately, fiercely, generously, and gracefully.

In the prologue to her encouraging book *In These Girls, Hope Is a Muscle*, journalist Madeleine Blais recalls that her childhood was virtually devoid of sports. A generation older than the teenagers on the Amherst, Massachusetts, high school basketball team she writes about, Blais realizes how different a childhood lacking sports can be: "During the fifties, gender division was practiced as a kind of apartheid . . . Leaving aside for the moment the question of whether I possessed any native athletic talent, which is doubtful, I acknowledge that there was nothing in my life of a team nature that supported even the free expression of brute energy, of which I have plenty." How unfortunate it was for Blais to miss out on the opportunity to explore her childhood potential, or at least to channel her energy. And how fortunate it is that this gender division, sportslessness for girls, now—thirty-five years after Title IX was passed—is so much less common.

Women gain strength and confidence from exploring their abilities in sports. Sports also help expand our view of ourselves. Girls need to be able to look at their bodies on occasion without gauging skirt size or magazine-photo worthiness. There's no avoiding the pressures on women to chase a movie-star look, as far as I can tell, but sports offer girls an alternate yardstick for measuring their value. Girls who play sports feel more confident; they're less likely to be depressed and are healthier, according to research conducted by the Women's Sports Foundation.

Sports can offer solace. Women's National Basketball Association (WNBA) star Tamika Catchings found a place—on the basketball court—where it didn't matter that her hearing was dependent on the blocky aids hooked over her ears and that her speech didn't sound like everyone else's; playing hoops, she could trounce any and all of the kids who teased her.

Sport makes us powerful.

Donna Lopiano, who competed nationally in softball, volleyball, field hockey, and basketball, and is now president of the Women's Sports Foundation, notes that we have seen an enormous shift in sports audiences and participation. "I don't think there's any question about the cultural change that occurred after Title IX—the magnitude of change in athletics has been extraordinary," she says. "The first generation to grow up under Title IX is not jaded about watching women play. You have men and women growing up respecting women's sports. And it's only going to get better. It's fun to watch as opportunity becomes something that women expect." Today, 30 percent of women identify themselves as sports fans. The audience for professional men's sports is on average from 35 to 45 percent female; the audience for women's sports is about 50 percent female. For the women's events at the 1996 Olympic games, the American television audience was 65 percent female.

Before Title IX, women's participation in college sports was at about 15 percent; only one in twenty-seven high school girls played sports. Today women make up more than 40 percent of college athletes, and one in three high school girls plays in a sports program. The emergence of the WNBA in the last ten years is another example of the growing popularity of women's sports. If only we could bring back the women's soccer league, as well. And, while we're at it, let's even out some of the financial disparities, from salary differences to sponsorship opportunities to television coverage.

It isn't, of course, what women can do *in comparison to men* that matters. It's simply what they can *do*. So perhaps it's a mistake to constantly measure women's athletics against men's in terms of achievement, participation, and attention. But it's easy to see, from any glance at a sports section or visit to a sports website, that women are entirely underrepresented.

Studying *The New York Times* Sunday sports section over the course of two months in the fall of 2006, I found the newspaper contained 282 images of men compared with 9 images of women. It's an admittedly unscientific sample, especially given that the time frame cuts through the heart of football season. But including 11 other photos that featured both men and women or no people at all, this tally indicates that women were represented visually in the section only 3 percent of the time. And studying column inches of text was no more encouraging, with nearly the same ratio: Of nearly two-thousand inches of column article text included in a month's worth of *The New York Times* Sunday sports sections, less than sixty inches were devoted to covering women's sports. These numbers show that sports writers in the section covered women athletes less than 3 percent of the time. This is outrageous: It would be easy to conclude that the sports section is simply not for women athletes, or anyone wanting to read about them.

This disparity is why Jane Gottesman was moved to organize her excellent exhibition of photographs of women athletes, *Game Face: What Does a Female Athlete Look Like?* A sports reporter, she assessed coverage in newspapers and *Sports Illustrated* through the early 1990s, and she writes in books, television, and magazines. "I found nothing that reflected the beautiful and complicated relationship women have to sports in a world where prescribed feminine behavior does not include the muscle, sweat, and passion that are ingrained elements of sport," Gottesman writes.

I was privileged to be able to view Gottesman's exhibit while working on the final sections of this book. In the show, one photo captures the American 400-meter relay team just after they won gold in the 1996 Olympics. All four of the runners—Gwen Torrence, Inger Miller, Gail Devers, and Chrystie Gaines—are laughing as they finish their victory lap, flags in hand, their legs sculpted with muscle. "We do things that give us more of a sense of power than the average woman," Torrence said about the image.

Feeling powerful gives an athlete the confidence to take risks and make changes. Big-wave surfer Jamilah Star would never be able to charge over the lip of the enormous waves she rides—up to fifty-foot faces—if she didn't believe in herself and in the power of her own courage.

The playing field has changed a lot over the last generation. Misty May-Treanor and her mother, Barbara, are perfect examples of this. Barbara competed in a parks and recreation volleyball league, the only one available to women at the time. Her daughter has competed around the world, winning a gold medal in Athens at the last Olympics.

The women in this book are champions in the greatest sense of the word. Not only are they competitors and disciplined athletes, but they are thoughtful people who make their sport, and their communities, better. Rhythmic gymnast Wendy Hilliard excelled in competition despite attempts to push her out of the sport, and later, as a coach, she started a foundation to give inner-city kids opportunities in gymnastics—and help integrate a racially lopsided sport. Open-water swimmer Lynne Cox didn't want to simply break records in her sport—something the natural athlete was remarkably gifted at. She took her goals to a new level, using the sport as a platform to make statements about clean water and peace between nations.

I hope you find the ten women profiled in these pages as amazing, inspiring, surprising, and thrilling as I did. They are role models of the highest caliber, ordinary women who elevated themselves with grit, skill, intellect—and a lot of passion, muscle, and sweat. They show us all how to take our dreams a little further, and I'm honored to add my voice to the choir singing their praises.

The Beauty of Power

Jamilah Star

Big-Wave Surfer Jamilah Star

Winner Billabong XXL Global Big Wave Women's Performance Award 2006 (Mavericks and Waimea Bay); winner Billabong XXL Global Big Wave Women's Monster Paddle Award 2005 (Waimea); second woman to surf Mavericks 2002, 2003, 2005; biggest paddle-in wave surfed by a woman 2003 (Waimea).

Along the water's edge of La Jolla Reefs, ten miles north of San Diego, big-wave surfer Jamilah Star is rocking the beach. And she's just warming up: We're jogging a half mile on the packed sand to a rocky turnaround point to loosen up before she heads in for a surf set on a clear, sunny day at Windansea, a break made famous for its rambunctious long-board scene in the 1950s. The waves are rolling easy and soft at about three to four feet. Around a dozen surfers are already out in the water—all of them men, though there's a woman in the parking lot above the rocks suiting up. Another dozen people are hanging around: A sun-leathered skinny man in a baseball cap and flip-flops studies the action from the overlook by the cars. Three teenage boys in shorts, two of them shirtless, are nudging the waves with their toes. A businessman is leaning against a boulder, eating his lunch, sandwich in one hand and plastic wrap balled in the other. Several more surfers are readying themselves and their boards to head out, or—dripping, hair plastered to foreheads, shoulders rounded in fatigue—are reluctantly leaving the powdery gold sand.

But everyone, for this suspended moment, has paused to watch twenty-eight-year-old Jamilah Star run down the beach. She is wearing a red bikini top and surfer shorts. She has long blond hair and sculpted muscles, and is deeply tanned. The coolio young surfers on the beach check her out furtively as they pretend to study their boards; the older man in the cap just gapes. It's a cinematic moment, time slowed down as our feet slap the sand, I feel myself flush, and everyone continues to stare. I realize this is an uncomfortable kind of power, being the focus of attention in this way, but Jamilah, astonishingly, is oblivious. She raises her arms in circles to stretch her shoulders and gazes at the waves.

"I can't wait to jump in the ocean," she says.

I murmur in agreement, though I'll just be wading as Jamilah surfs.

"Jumping in the ocean feels like going home. Growing up, I always thought of the ocean as my home and my family," she continues.

I glance at her face, but no, I don't think she's faking nonchalance. Jamilah has no inkling of the ripple effect her warm-up jog is having on this crowd. She isn't concerned about anyone on the beach because she's absorbed in studying the waves.

Surfing has contributed a lot to popular culture, spawning its own (awesome) vocabulary, multiple fashion lines (Ocean Pacific and Roxy profiting nicely), and cinematic memorables (Sandra Dee as Gidget to *Fast Times at Ridgemont High*'s party animal Jeff Spicoli to surfer Keala Kennelly as herself in *Blue Crush*). It's easy to think, from magazines, books, and movies, that surfing is more a lifestyle than a sport. The skill involved in catching and riding the ocean's surges has sometimes been overlooked in the interest of celebrating the surfing personality. But attitude trumps athleticism only to outsiders. Anyone who has tried to paddle out on a board past the whitewater crash of the impact zone and sat in the water hoping to time start kick, wave surge, and pop up while staying in control immediately realizes that willingness, desire, and even innate coolness will only get you so far—and where these qualities on their own will take you is likely headfirst into damp sand. Still, the surfing myth endures. This is the dream: Surfers are mellow, happy, free, and—due to lots of sun, sand, swimming, and living the aloha spirit—beautiful.

The pressure to look the part is greatest on surfer chicks. Of course. Why would surfing be different from everything else? Everyone at the beach today is probably watching Jamilah because she's, simply, hot. *Maybe* it's also because she's the hottest up-and-coming big-wave surfer around, one of the boldest athletes on the planet. She won the Billabong XXL Global Big Wave Award in 2005 and 2006, the first years the contest included a women's category. She's widely acknowledged as having surfed the largest wave ever paddled into by a woman. And she was the second woman to tackle the fierce conditions at Mavericks, the famously dangerous cold-water, heavy-wave, shark-infested break south of San Francisco. She is leading the future's next wave of big-wave chargers: women.

We finish up our run, and Jamilah grabs her board to head out. "Power is really intimidating," she says. She could be talking about the ocean, or herself. "For most people."

A certain bravado is required to tackle monster waves, water that soars three, four, even five stories above your head with indescribable force. Surfers can practice riding lesser surf; they can train to get themselves in shape; and they can visualize the waves. But eventually they run out of simulated experiences, and if they want to test their mettle they have to dive in. And at that point—all big-wave riders agree on this issue—it's like nothing else they've ever done.

When Billabong first began offering its Global Big Wave Awards in 2000, the event tracked an explosive development in the sport. The advent of tow-in surfing—using a Jet Ski or other personal watercraft to ride into a wave—blew the ceiling off of surfing's ultimate limits. Before tow-in, a surfer was limited by his or her ability to paddle out into a wave and accelerate enough to catch it; even surfers are only so strong. And generally, the bigger a wave, the faster it travels. Even as aerial tricks and wave-face maneuvers gained the most acclaim on the pro circuit in the 1980s, a certain group of surfers sought to ride bigger and bigger waves. They were testing their abilities against endlessly powerful forces in an age-old matchup: man versus nature. This is a fundamental aspect of the sport, going back to big-wave pioneers Wally Froiseth, John Kelly, and George Downing at Oʻahu's Makaha break in the late 1930s. Its source is the same primal urge that spurs mountain climbers and Antarctic adventurers to see how far they can go. But by using motorized watercraft to ride into ever-larger waves, a technique popularized by golden boy and big-wave champion Laird Hamilton, surfers were no longer limited by the strength of their arms.

The Guinness World Record for the largest wave paddled into and surfed successfully is held by Southern California native Taylor Knox, at a break called Killers in Todos Santos near Ensenada, Mexico, in 1998. Guinness records do not have a category—yet—for women surfers. Last year, Brad Gerlach won the big-wave award at the same break, where he and partner Mike Parsons towed into a wave measured (by studying photos) to be sixty-eight feet. He was awarded $1,000 for every foot of wave height, totaling $68,000—one of the largest individual prizes in the sport. The previous year, Dan Moore won for a wave that was also judged to be sixty-eight feet high, this one at Jaws off the coast of Maui; he caught it with tow partner Mark Anderson. Customarily, a surfer will share the prize with his partner; tow-in surfing is really a team sport, with at least two people (and often more) needed to drive the watercraft and to be on hand in case a rescue is needed. Most duos take turns on the waves, so a contest winner is the lucky one who caught the biggest in a set of waves of a particular high-surf day. The awards also include prizes for largest paddle-in wave, biggest tube ridden, general performance, most spectacular wipeout, and, for the last two years, best overall performance for women. This is where Jamilah comes in; the award brought her recognition beyond the small world of big-wave surfing.

The Billabong XXL contest has gotten a lot of attention beyond surf circles. It plays well to the general public because its concept is simple: acknowledge the biggest and bravest. The elements are easy to understand, even if you know little about surfing. "Some of the judging criteria in standard surfing competitions are a little esoteric for people that don't live and breathe the sport," says Bill Sharp, event director for the XXL awards. "When you boil it down to 'biggest wave wins,' people can get their heads around it."

Measuring wave heights is not an exact science. The ocean is, of course, always moving. Jamilah and many others on the islands use what's called the Hawaiian method to estimate the size of a wave. It's a system whose source is unclear: Most surfers explain the Hawaiian method as an assessment of the distance from the highest point on the wave crest to the lowest point at the wave's *back,* but a wave's backside is pretty difficult to see from shore. Others say the Hawaiian scale has evolved out of the inherent modesty of the surfer code, whereby wave height is always cut down to avoid boastfulness. Regardless of its origins, the Hawaiian method has smaller numbers than a second, more straightforward method, estimating face height from the trough—the lowest point in front of the wave—to the wave's peak. Generally, doubling a Hawaiian wave measurement will get you close to this face-height estimate. But this is a somewhat clumsy guess, and it gets more skewed as the wave gets larger.

For the Global Big Wave awards, judges use photographs of the rider to estimate the wave's face and total height. In past years, some finalists have been judged to be riding waves of nearly equal height, and in that case the judges favor the rider on the more difficult wave—be it heavier or steeper or hollower or more challenging in some way. "The whole event is based on the photographic evidence," explains Sharp. "In the case of no photographer, it's like a giant tree falling in the woods without a witness: It didn't occur." This diverges from surfing's storytelling tradition, in which tales about tackling giant waves, such as Greg Noll's epic ride on Makaha in the massive storm of 1969, have been handed down to each new generation on beaches around the world. Surfing's oral tradition has given way to photographic documentation.

Jamilah grew up listening to this oral history in the surf-happy town of Santa Cruz, California, on the state's central coast, sixty miles south of San Francisco. It's a city famous for redwood trees, jealously guarded surf breaks, and the historic wooden roller coaster along its popcorn- and sand-littered boardwalk. It became Jack O'Neill's home after he started developing early neoprene wetsuits, and it houses the first surf museum in the country. The most famous monument in town is a bronze replica of a surfer with his towering longboard at the cliffs above a gentle break popular with beginners.

The statue often sports seasonal adornment, a tropical lei in spring or an evergreen wreath in December.

Jamilah's parents were teenagers when she was born. Her father, Reve Fuse, an avid surfer, bought her a board when she was five. On her first ride she smacked her head, cut it open, and had to be taken to the emergency room for stitches. That's not what stands out in her memory, though. What she remembers most clearly is her father's reaction to her first stand-up: "When I caught my first wave, my dad and all his friends saw. That was the beginning of the end for me. I remember his face so vividly; I had never seen him so proud," she says. She also remembers hurrying back from the hospital so they wouldn't miss a friend's party.

Growing up, Jamilah loved sports, anything that challenged her natural strength. She was the only girl on the boys' wrestling team at Santa Cruz High School. She played varsity waterpolo. And she spent a lot of afternoons surfing at Steamer Lane, the world-class break around Lighthouse Point where the O'Neill Cold Water Classic competitions have been held since the mid-1980s. When she was seventeen, she saw her first video of Jeff Clark surfing the famed massive break Mavericks, about twenty-five miles up the coast from her hometown. "The minute I saw that video, I decided that's what I wanted to do with my life," she says. "That was before any woman had surfed it." Five years later, California native Sarah Gerhardt, at age twenty-three, became the first woman to tackle the jaw-dropping wave.

Jamilah sees big-wave surfing as a natural evolution of her surfing style. In her late teens and early twenties, she competed in Costa Rica and Santa Cruz and had some big successes, winning the Central American longboard circuit in 2002, when she competed against men, and the professional competition at her home break in 2001. But competitive surfing, in which points are awarded to the trickiest aerial maneuvers and flashy wave-carving techniques, didn't interest her as much as seeking out the biggest waves she could find. She liked paddling into massive surf on her longboard. You could call her a surfing traditionalist—except for the fact that she's breaking barriers as a woman.

When Jamilah was twenty-three, she moved to O'ahu to hone her skills riding big waves. The northern part of the island, called the North Shore, has Sunset Beach's heavy waves and Waimea's fearsome drops. Though it is said that the bottom two-thirds of Waimea's big waves aren't so difficult, according to Surfline.com writer Jason Borte, its watery cliff edge of a start requires "a set of bowling balls in your trunks." Macho talk didn't stop Jamilah from setting her sights on these waves. But shortly after the move, she learned that her mother, Wendy, was sick with advanced ovarian cancer. She didn't know what to do, whether to stay and train or to move back to care for her mom, who didn't have anyone else.

Jamilah's parents split up when she was five, and she was raised by her father and his family. Relations between her mother and her father were strained. "Basically my family kind of stole me from her," she says. "My dad was just doing his best. He wanted me to be away from drugs and all that."

Her mother was addicted to heroin and spent a good part of her adult life homeless. Wendy "wasn't interested in dealing with society," as Jamilah puts it. The two of them would sometimes meet up on the streets of Santa Cruz to hang out and talk. They were close despite seeing each other irregularly.

In November that year, a big swell was headed to the North Shore. It was her first chance to test her skills on the big waves she'd been training for. More than most athletes, a surfer is at the mercy of the seasons and the storms. But Jamilah was worried about her mom.

"Do you want me to come home?" she asked her mom over the phone. But Wendy just wanted her to describe Hawaii. Jamilah told her mother how beautiful it was, how warm the water was, and about her training at Waimea Bay.

"You know what, angel," Wendy said, "I think you should stay there. I think you can surf that big wave."

The next day, the biggest swell of the year hit the North Shore. "But I was so not afraid. It was almost like she was with me," Jamilah says. She surfed Waimea Bay's twenty-foot faces, the biggest she'd tackled yet. Then she flew home to see her mother.

Waves get big when they cross suddenly from deep ocean to a shallow, irregular sea floor, and that's exactly what happens at Mavericks, a half mile offshore from Pillar Point near the town of Half Moon Bay in Northern California. The submerged reef serves up large waves with a long barrel tube and a thick curl. Hundreds of rocks edge the shore in an area called "the boneyard." The cold water creates a dense wave (molecules grouping closer together at colder temperatures) that can pin a surfer below the surface for too long—which is what happened, tragically, to accomplished big-wave surfer Mark Foo in 1994 on a twenty-foot wave.

For years, Half Moon Bay locals who had seen the storm-generated winter waves offshore from a hard-to-reach beach proclaimed them unsurfable. But in 1975, local Jeff Clark charged the waves here, and, after fifteen years of secretly riding on his own, he shared the location of this monster wave with a few friends from Santa Cruz. When word got out, surfers were shocked; no one thought California could offer epic waves to rival Hawaii. Now, Quiksilver sponsors an annual Men Who Ride Mountains invitational contest here every winter that features twenty top athletes, intense media attention, and a purse of $75,000.

The winter of her mother's death, Jamilah tackled Mavericks, her life's goal, becoming the second woman to ride the break. When she's training for a certain spot, Jamilah spends time meditating on and visualizing the wave. She gets herself to an intense state of focus. "I do physical preparation for years before I approach the situations. I know the level of power I'll face. The night before, I light candles and pray and stay super centered. When I go out to the beach, I've been planning it for years," Jamilah says.

On that morning in January, the buoys were over twenty-one feet at seventeen-second intervals. That's "a good bit of water," as Jamilah understates it. At the beach, she saw a group of local surfers towing in on personal watercraft; she was going to paddle in. She got her wetsuit on and looked up, but the guys had disappeared. She was "super focused, super calm" as she got in the water, she says. "I noticed the swell was a little bit bigger. The southerly current was predominant. I got sucked in. *I need to streamline,* I thought, *I'll head to the mushroom rock then veer out to the channel.* I couldn't see the guys, I was all alone. I got a little to the outside and got sucked to the left. I got worked by whitewater over and over again. I kept ditching the board and diving under. *Wow, this is pretty amazing,* I thought. All of a sudden I started to worry. I was thinking, *Should I really try to go in?* I started sweating."

Paddling past the whitewater onslaught is incredibly hard work. As a wave's overall height grows, the amount of energy it contains increases at an exponential rate. And waves pack a huge punch: Oceanographers estimate that a single wave of four feet striking along North America's West Coast would release fifty million horsepower. Jamilah was fighting a lot of force pushing her back toward the beach.

As she paddled out, she started to feel a little frightened and very alone. "I felt really desolate. *God has me here for a reason,* I thought. *If I'm not meant to make it out, I won't.* All of a sudden six guys paddled up behind me. I thought they had passed me, but I had actually passed them. We all started making it through, over the falls. Then I was super relaxed, thinking, *This is no big deal.*"

The waves were enormous, more than twenty-five feet Hawaiian. "I was praying to get a wave right away. Then I thought, *I need to try to let go of my ego. It's just great that I'm out here.* One wave I almost went for, but I knew I wasn't going to make it. One of the guys gave me a hard time. 'Why didn't you go?' he asked. But sometimes they just give me a hard time, they're a little bit jealous of my strength. Another guy caught a huge wave. *Okay,* I thought, *I can do this; I grew up with these guys.* A set came through and I saw my wave. Maybe there were seven guys on the inside bowl, I was on the middle bowl. I started paddling and air-dropped in between those guys. The next thing I knew, the whole face of the wave was turquoise. I remembered my coach's voice in my head, 'Stay low, stay low.' The wave kept bounding and bounding, it turned to dark blue, then it blew up and turned silver. And I kicked out. It was the best wave of my life."

Though she has made a name for herself in the surf world, Jamilah leads an improvised, impulsive life. She didn't have a dollar of extra cash when she traveled to California for the Global Big Wave Awards ceremony last year. "If I hadn't won, I don't know how I would have gotten back home," she says. Yet she gave a big chunk of her $5,000 prize money to her family and teammates—flying her dad to Hawaii so the two of them could surf together, buying her husband, Ariel Sanchez, a ticket to visit his daughter on the mainland, helping fellow surfers in Hawaii to get by. She surfed for years with very little money and no sponsors, spending a season riding on a board with a broken fin that she "had to stomp on" to keep balanced in the water. "I learned to survive without sponsors," she says. "I knew I would make it with or without support. But I thought, *If I surf the biggest wave in the world, then they'll notice me.*" Today, she has sponsorship from one organization, a sports drink company.

I met up with Jamilah in La Jolla because she'd had to delay a surfing trip to Costa Rica when she realized, en route from Honolulu, that she'd lost her passport. She easily makes the best of it: Camped out at her agent's house until the new passport comes through, she borrowed a board to surf, and this is enough to make her happy. "It'll work out," she says about her travel plans.

Her world is largely self-invented. Born Jamilah Istfan Haje, she changed her name to Jamilah Star as she began big-wave surfing; teammates call her JamStar. She developed a strong spirituality, an amalgam of traditional religions, though her family "was atheist." When I ask Jamilah what gear she travels with, she responds, "First of all, I always have God. That's the most important. It's a God that I've found on my own. This God is a universal energy. It's not one God: Ja, Elijah, you can say anything you want. After this Earth we're going somewhere; there's heaven on this planet, too. Basically, I don't worship anything negative."

Jamilah has carved out a typically iconoclastic path in competitions, too, eschewing the pro women's circuit in favor of her passion for big waves. The wave she charged in Waimea in 2003, estimated by the crowd as close to a fifty-foot face, really forced the Billabong Global Big Wave judges to establish a women's category, which they did the following year. A few surfers grumbled to me that the 2003 wave should have received acknowledgment since it was likely the biggest paddle-in ride of that season. But for that inaugural women's prize of $5,000, Jamilah was nominated for four different waves; two teammates, Kim Hamrock and Jennifer Useldinger, were her competitors. And in 2006, when Jamilah won again, she was up against just one other woman finalist, Keala Kennelly, for an impressive tow-in set at Tahiti's Teahupoo. Judges established the women's category as an overall performance award for the season. For the men's awards, paddle-in and tow-in categories are separate. And the women were competing for one $5,000 award, while the men's categories included the $68,000 big-wave prize, a $10,000 monster-paddle prize, and a couple of $5,000 awards. The discrepancy rubs Jamilah the wrong way: "How can you offer girls only $5,000?" she asks. But, others point out that there are quite a lot more men braving monster waves. And event director Bill Sharp notes that the big-wave award is open to women, though none have surfed at that level just yet. It's anybody's guess, he says, how long it will be before a woman makes it to the finals. On that score, many would agree with longtime surfer and watercraft safety expert Shawn Alladio, who told *Surf Life for Women,* "Jamilah is the one to watch."

As she has gotten more successful, Jamilah has made an effort to help other women surfers. She shares a house on the North Shore with her husband and coach, Sanchez, as well as a rotating group of five or six teammates. "I thought if I wanted to have girls to surf with, maybe I better train them myself," she says. "I saw so many girls who deserve to have the opportunity. But there were no doors open to them. They didn't understand what they could do."

The women's field has grown in the last decade—even as it remains tiny compared to the men's. Two years ago, North Shore surfer Betty Depolito, nicknamed Banzai Betty for her bold rides at Waimea and Sunset during the 1980s, established a women's big-wave contest at the North Shore's Pipeline break, site of an iconic men's competition since the 1970s. "It's a step up for the women to just have a contest there," she says. She knows it's a challenge for many of the women to catch enough big waves to raise their skills to the elite level. "You have to be pretty aggressive to get a wave from any of those guys," Depolito says. "You're not only out there hassling with the wave itself. The guys are so much stronger physically; they're capable of taking off deeper in the wave. They're crazier. They'll take off on anything. Women are more finesse oriented."

Big-wave surfers are a bold group. They risk their lives every time they go out—no matter how skilled and experienced a surfer is, there's no guarantee of safety in the ocean. "There aren't a lot of big-wave surfers who don't believe in God," is how Jamilah puts it. In the surf-history film *Riding Giants,* one of Waimea Bay's big-wave pioneers, Ricky Grigg, discusses his own experience with the risks: "I can remember fracturing my neck at Waimea. I hit the water and my neck went back in a whiplash. I lost all feeling in my arms and legs. I was like a seagull full of oil just fluttering in the whitewater," he says. "And some guys came over and helped me in. I'm lucky to be alive. And I think every single big-wave surfer could tell you a story like that."

To improve in a sport, an athlete has to reach beyond his or her current limits. But in big-wave surfing there's a scary line between pushing your skills and getting in over your head. Excellent surfers are hurt or killed every year, some on not-so-large waves. Big-wave surfing is not something to try lightly. Every surfer I've ever talked to gets worked up about this subject. Bill Sharp of the XXL awards stresses that the contest is by no means encouragement for unprepared fame-seekers to foolishly risk their lives, and this is why it is by invitation only. "We need to make it crystal clear that this isn't a bounty," he says. "This isn't *Jackass*. The event was created to be a reflection of what's going on in the sport of big-wave surfing as opposed to being an engine. You have to know what you're doing."

Jamilah trained for years to face Waimea, Sunset, and Mavericks. She's also tackled Jaws, though not at peak waves—"so I'm not going to claim anything," she says. But I sensed a level of wariness in the reactions of a handful of the other surfers who talked about her achievements. "She has rhinoceros strength," one longtime Santa Cruz surfer told me. "But she might not have the skills." This is possibly true, but who's to say what Jamilah's ultimately capable of? Maybe this reluctance reflects the general wariness of a group that understands the inherent risks in big-wave surfing. Maybe it's a generation gap, senior wave riders naturally reluctant to cede territory to up-and-coming athletes. Maybe it's Jamilah's Northern California brand of optimism and openness—which can come across at first as naïveté. Or maybe it's discomfort or unfamiliarity with a woman who radiates a level of ambition and confidence more often found in a man.

The group out in the water at Windansea is lined up for the small sets. The waves are breaking to the right (from the surfers' point of view), with the rider closest to the whitewater's edge holding the right of way. The surfers take turns; many walk up and down on their longboards, touching their toes to the shoreside end. They make it look easy. The waves are mild and stretched out, offering a nice long ride before they crash into the sand. It's not hard to pick Jamilah out of the crowd, which now numbers about fifteen. She rides athletically, with her legs bent, crouched down a bit lower than the other surfers. Her hair is in a ponytail. She's one of two women, and the only one not in a wetsuit. She says she developed a pretty thick skin from surfing most of her childhood without a wetsuit in the cold waters of Santa Cruz. San Diego's waves, in comparison, are fairly comfortable. She takes the next wave, rides back over the edge as it fizzles out, and then jumps into the water to paddle out. Then I can't find her. Surfers bob in the ocean; a few others grab waves. I am confused when I pick out Jamilah's board some moments later with an odd-looking surfer aboard. It is only when she gets close that I realize Jamilah looks funny because she's riding the wave while doing a headstand. Her legs kick to the sky and she coasts in.

In the parking lot, the older man with the baseball cap says hello. He knows Jamilah. "I surfed with your dad," he says. "You were looking good out there." Jamilah smiles.

The man nods like he has something more to say, holding himself with the self-appointed authority of a Sunday NFL couch-coach. "But you're too far back on your board."

Jamilah cocks her head. The man looks her up and down; she's dripping wet in her bikini.

"You're looking good. But you need to move up on your board. Your balance is a little off."

She puts her board in the back of the PT Cruiser.

"Looking good," he says. "Just move up. You'll have more control. Looking good!"

Another guy, Jamilah's age, comes over. He knows Jamilah from Santa Cruz. "You surfed with her dad," he says to the older man. "Right on." To Jamilah, he says, "I hear you got some good waves in Tahiti."

She nods enthusiastically. "I got raked on the reefs." She'd been practicing tow-in surfing, developing her skills to be ready to face ever-larger waves. She turns to show him the lines of black scars across her back; it looks like one of the mythic siren's claws caught her in the water. All of us wince at the injury.

"I don't care, though," she says quickly. "It was so beautiful there."

We are ready to go, but the older man has stepped up, blocking Jamilah's way into the car. "Remember to move up on your board," he says again. "Looking good. Just move up on your board."

"So why do you keep telling me I'm looking good then?" Jamilah finally snaps.

The man is flustered. He doesn't know what to say; I think he'd intended to be helpful. I'm uncomfortable; clearly, being corrected in front of a journalist adds to Jamilah's irritation. As we drive away, Jamilah confesses, "A year ago, that comment would have made me cry."

She does cry, though, later that afternoon, as we talk about her mother over sandwiches at a café. "My mom thought I was an angel from heaven here to save the world," Jamilah says. She was able to make it home to Santa Cruz days before Wendy died. Her mother was unconscious, worn out from chemotherapy and drug therapy and from the illness that was sapping her strength. Jamilah told her about the big waves she'd surfed, though her mom was so sick she wasn't able to respond. Jamilah sat in the hospital room and described her plans to tackle Mavericks. And how she would use what she'd learned from that monster wave to tackle other big breaks. Jamilah said she would keep surfing until she found the biggest wave in the world and her achievement would be impossible to ignore. And here Jamilah's eyes fill with tears. "When I think about what I do, what might happen to me surfing—I think, *It's easy compared to heroin addiction, right?* Nothing's as bad as losing your mom."

Riding Snowflakes

Julie Krone

Jockey
Julie Krone

3,704 race wins, the most of any woman jockey in horse-racing history; 21,411 lifetime races, with $90,122,764 in purses; 300 stakes races wins; first and only woman jockey in Thoroughbred Racing's Hall of Fame (inducted 2000); first woman jockey to win at a Triple Crown event at the Belmont Stakes 1993 (on Colonial Affair); first woman jockey to win at a Breeders' Cup event 2003 (on Halfbridled).

It was a drizzly day in Elmont, New York, when jockey Julie Krone sped into history at thirty-six miles an hour, setting a record at the Belmont Stakes (also known as the "Run for the Carnations") as the first woman to ride in a winner. That first Saturday of June in 1993, the twenty-nine-year-old Julie sat in red and gold silks astride a huge bay with a black mane and tail called Colonial Affair. At seventeen hands (sixty-eight inches to the withers), he was the largest in the group of thirteen starters. And he was a longshot, with 13 to 1 odds to win.

In the walk to the starting gate, Julie had touched Colonial Affair's neck, pausing before the forty-five thousand spectators to get a sense of how he was taking the cold rain and the mood at the track. Colonial Affair liked a crowd and was feeling confident, she could tell; he was ready to run. They lined up, and when the gate opened, Colonial Affair jumped out. Julie kept him inside, where the track is shortest. Her goal was to get her stallion wanting the win, to hold him until the right moment to unleash his speed. Dirt from the leaders' hooves flew into her mount's eyes. She knew he wanted to get out from under the stinging hail of dirt clods, but she made him wait. The Belmont is the longest of the three Triple Crown races, a quarter mile longer than the Kentucky Derby and a quarter mile plus a furlong longer than the Preakness Stakes. At one lap around the enormous Belmont track, the one-and-a-half-mile distance is unfamiliar to most of the three-year-olds running. Pacing is crucial.

Julie knew she had a lot of horse beneath her, a rocket on the track. She stayed patient. On the backstretch, Julie saw a spot she liked away from the rail. She moved Colonial Affair out. They were in tenth place. But now Colonial Affair's line was clear; the other horses were no longer blocking his way. He could see light ahead.

The racehorses were breathing hard; the sound of their hooves on the dirt track was enormous, like a rapid throbbing heartbeat pulsing from the ground. With three furlongs to go, less than a quarter mile, she gave the horse a chirp and threw her reins.

And Colonial Affair "sprouted wings," as she says in her memoir, *Riding for My Life.* They won by two and a quarter lengths.

That day, Julie became the first woman jockey to win a Triple Crown race. She had worked hard for thirteen years to perform in the hot-blooded, testosterone-filled sport of horse racing. She had talked her way onto horses with trainers who didn't believe in girl jockeys. She had bounced back from a broken back, a broken arm, and enough bruises and scrapes to cover every inch of her four-foot ten-inch frame several times over. She had dropped out of high school and lied about her age to get her start as a jockey; she'd snuck onto a track to find a job; she'd made the rounds, sleeping on pull-out couches in generic apartments from Michigan to Florida to Maryland to New Jersey and back again.

She had used every bit of her energy and ambition and fire and pluck to get to that winner's circle. Only four other women had ever ridden in any of the Triple Crown events; none but Julie had ridden in the 126-year-old Belmont Stakes. None had won before. Rising from the victory blanket of white carnations draped across Colonial Affair's withers was the sweet, vindicating smell of success.

Twenty-year racing veteran Julie Krone is known for her timing. Her signature approach is patience: She waits, midpack, keeping her horse relaxed, as she looks for an inside window to slip through or a spot outside. At the right moment, she'll jump ahead for the win in the homestretch. She makes a sudden, calculated burst of speed at the finish. Horse racing, of course, is all about being in the right place at the right time.

Off the track, however, she has not built a reputation for her patience. Rather, her explosive behavior has gotten her in the news. Early on, she retaliated with her fists when she struck another jockey on her mount during a race; another rider who'd lost to her whipped her ear, slicing the skin, and that battle ended up with a wrestling match in a swimming pool. One jockey who rode too close to her on the track ended up with several fewer teeth. As recently as 2003, months before her retirement at age forty-one, she was fined for "acting in an unprofessional manner" with a fellow jockey after a race in which the other rider had ridden unsafely.

The jockeys' world is a hard one to break into, especially for a young girl. Julie grew up on a horse farm outside Eau Claire,

Michigan, a town of fewer than a thousand people not far from the shores of Lake Michigan and the football powerhouse of Notre Dame University in South Bend, Indiana. The area is known for its fruit farms, sand dunes, and the South Shore railroad line, which transports summering Chicago residents to the beach.

When Julie's mother told a friend that her daughter wanted to be a jockey, the friend said she should go home and smack her daughter on the head for foolish ideas. It wasn't until 1968, when Julie was five years old, that the first woman jockey was licensed to ride in the United States—after Kathy Kusner (a future Olympic equestrian) filed a sex discrimination lawsuit against the Maryland Race Commission to force the issue. Opportunities for women had not opened up much wider when Julie first hit the track eleven years later. But ever since she could see the four-legged animals on her family's farm, Julie loved horses. She loved riding fast. She loved racing. When she was fourteen, she watched jockey Steve Cauthen win the Kentucky Derby astride Affirmed and decided on her life's career. She simply would not entertain the thought that she didn't belong in the world of horse racing.

Julie was a bit "wild" as a child, she says. She and her older brother, Donnie, spent most of their days wandering in the fields and woods, exploring with their pony, Filly, and their Arabian horse, Ralphy. Julie liked to race Ralphy around their property while she stood on his back; she would drop to a seated position just before running into the barn, so that she wouldn't be decapitated at the door. She also liked to do backflips off Ralphy's back end. Julie taught Filly to sit, roll over, and bow, as if she were a dog. Filly was a half-Shetland, half-Arabian pony and "100 percent diabolical," Julie says.

Shetlands are famous for their stubborn natures, Arabians for their spirit. Filly was a tough combination: She was "elusive, naughty, and at times downright mean," Julie says in *Riding for My Life*. "If I tied her to a fence, she'd chew through the rope and get loose. And when I rode her, she would constantly plot ways to buck me off. Sometimes Filly would get so angry with me for trying to train her that she would throw herself on the ground or sit back on her hind legs and then jump into the air and take off bucking." The pony's willful personality taught her how to work with ornery animals. "I credit Filly with teaching me to ride well," Julie writes.

Julie's parents were not ones for conventional routines. Julie never had a curfew or a bedtime, and her family never sat down for a family dinner around the dining room table. Her meals usually consisted of a peanut butter sandwich at a perch in her favorite tree or lingering at a friend's until the friend's mother offered home cooking.

Her mother, Judi Krone, specialized in dressage, the elegant European riding style sometimes called "horse ballet." Her children inherited her love of horses. Donnie went on to work at tracks in Maryland. And Judi was supportive of her daughter's ambitions— though Julie wanted to be a jockey so fiercely, her mother likely had no choice. She enrolled Julie in a horsemanship clinic near their home, and both were encouraged when the instructor, well-known in his field, admired her skills and encouraged her dream of becoming a jockey. He laid out a plan of action for her (buy books and magazines to learn about the sport, find a trainer, get a job at a track), and Judi and Julie followed his suggestions to the letter. At home at night, the two of them pored over horse magazines and jockey biographies. Judi saved tips from her second job as a waitress, and her daughter taught riding for extra cash so the two could travel to Louisville, Kentucky, during the spring break of Julie's sophomore year in high school, to work at Churchill Downs, the site of the Kentucky Derby. Neither had held a job at a racetrack before, but both mother and daughter worked as "hot-walkers," bathing and cooling down horses after races. With a birth certificate predated by three months to make her a legal employee, Julie returned to the track that summer, living with trainers Clarence and Donna Picou, to work as a hot-walker and groom.

Julie loved being at the track. She loved the excitement of the races; she loved being around horses. She worshipped the jockeys Steve Cauthen, Angel Cordero, and Bill Shoemaker. She dreamed constantly of riding and racing.

She was not as enthusiastic about school. She found out much later that she had dyslexia and other learning disorders, but in high school all she knew was that she felt stuck, like she couldn't learn. Her parents divorced when she was fourteen; her older brother moved out. And Julie dropped out of high school midway through her senior year to move to Tampa, Florida, to become a jockey. Her mother sent her south with relatives, then regretted her decision and took a bus to meet her daughter there. The two of them snuck onto the track at Tampa Bay Downs the first day, climbing a fence because they didn't have the required passes for admission. They ran into some trainers who were friendly enough to humor the ambition of the tiny, blond girl with the high, squeaky voice. Until they saw her ride. Then, convinced by her skills, they got her the licenses she needed and she had a job.

Confident that her daughter was well on her way, Judi returned to Michigan. Her daughter spent the next six-month "meet"—a track's racing season—absorbing all the information she could. She had her first win in February. Afterward in the jocks' room, her fellow riders covered her with peanut butter, baby powder, shaving cream, and any other goopy stuff they could find—the traditional congratulations. She was thrilled.

But it was often tough to convince trainers and owners to let her ride their horses. Horse racing is a highly competitive world.

She had little experience. Owners don't like to take risks with their very expensive animals. She was small, smaller even than the average jockey by several inches. And she was a girl.

"Horse racing used to be an entirely male field, and on a scale of one to ten, its masculinity quotient remains about an eight," writes horse lover and novelist Jane Smiley in her book *A Year at the Races*. "The dominant culture remains competitive, secretive, individualistic, and focused on money."

A jockey is usually an independent contractor, vying for offers from the top stables. A jockey's agent negotiates for the rider, working for business from the best trainers with the best horses, the ones most likely to win and generate purses. It's a classic catch-22—to win, a jockey needs to ride winners; to ride winners, a jockey must first win. And to make money, a jockey absolutely must win. Jockeys get 10 percent of the race winnings; the agent gets about a quarter of the jockey's take. An agent has to juggle the rider's multiple commitments, often with mounts from a number of different barns on the same day, and sometimes acts as a bit of a wheeler and dealer, promising the rider to one horse, then "spinning" that commitment when a better offer comes along.

It takes a few years for a jockey to move up in the ranks. As a beginning "baby rider," with what's called a "bug"—or an asterisk— by her name in the program, Julie worked on selling her ability to ride to anyone who would listen. She was determined. She finished out the season at Tampa Bay, then went to Maryland to live with her new agent, Chick Lang, Jr. He rolled his eyes when he arrived at the airport to pick up her and her bags—which consisted of three cardboard boxes. And he rolled his eyes again when she cooed over the bright lights and big-city structures of suburban Timonium, Maryland.

At Pimlico Race Course, outside Baltimore, Julie knew nobody. She had to start all over again, befriending trainers, doing her best to charm them and sell her strengths despite their skepticism. She rode longshot after longshot, often coming in dead last. But she tried to ride each time as expertly and professionally as possible. And after a while she established herself. A well-known trainer with a talented stable asked her to ride for him. It was the leg up she needed. She had some wins, then had some more. She made the rounds of the racetracks of New Jersey: Atlantic City, Monmouth, Meadowlands, and Garden State Park. She was tops for wins in the season at three of the tracks. Then she moved to the big time: New York. And she tied her hero Angel Cordero (as well as Hall of Fame jockey Ron Turcotte) for a record five wins in one day at Saratoga Springs. She had the top number of wins at Belmont Park in 1993. She set a new record for number of wins by a female jockey, then kept pushing that number higher.

Julie's strength as a rider was her rapport with the horses. She had spent so much of her life with horses, she understood them. She could read their behavior. She knew what to do to urge them to run. "It's the attention to small details, like if a horse moves its ear or drops its head, or if a horse expresses itself with its body," she says. "Knowing how to react to that helps the horse and human get done what they have to get done."

Trainers like to talk about Julie's "magic hands," her ability to turn a promising but unproven horse into a confirmed winner. It's a matter of getting the horse to want to win, Julie would say. Scotty Schulhofer, trainer of Colonial Affair and many other horses that Julie rode, commented to *The New York Times,* "She talks to the horses in body language. They respond to her. She's a very smart girl, with a great feel. I think she's got the finest sense of horses of anyone around." Schulhofer admits that he is one of the trainers who, early on, thought a girl jockey just wouldn't work for his barn.

Julie is known for her light touch and her long, relaxed grip on the reins. In her memoir, Julie explains her approach as a jockey: "A few days before a race, I breeze the horse, get to know him. I place my hands and distribute my weight in ways that make him run better. If he's a nervous horse, I put my hands back by his withers, only pull a tiny bit when he pulls, give and relax when he gives and relaxes, and make sure I don't squeeze him with my legs or move my arms too much. There are twenty different movements I'll try in my first thirty seconds on that horse. When I find something that works, that brings him back between my hands and legs, I remember to use that movement during the race and hope that the horse can remember it, too."

Fellow jockey Richard Migliore told *The New York Times*, "Julie is an extremely patient rider. She just sits there with a long hold, not moving much, and the horses respond. I could ride like that till the cows come home and I wouldn't get that result."

Julie is quick to say there's no magic in her hands. She stresses that a rider should never get too confident. "When you're working with horses, you're constantly honing your skills. You never say to yourself, 'Oh, I'm so good,' or some horse is going to slap you upside the head," she says. "They're like snowflakes. They're always going to challenge you. It's endless. You have to be open to learning all the time."

In Maryland and New Jersey, Julie's dreams were coming true. She moved up from a baby jockey to an apprentice and then to journeyman rider, a fully licensed professional. Though she'd gotten noticed by some of the most powerful decision makers at the track, she was still young and brash. She says she had to learn how to be respectful of the others she worked around. She admits she made some early mistakes.

In the winter of 1982, just as she was emerging at Pimlico, track officials found marijuana in Julie's car. She was suspended for sixty days and had to attend a rehab program. She had fallen into a circle of friends who were smoking pot and using cocaine. Coke has been a drug of choice for a lot of jockeys trying to keep their weight down. Julie never struggled with her weight, but she had been smoking pot since she was about twelve years old.

Rehab forced her to admit she had a problem. That was the first step to getting clean, she says. And she absolutely had to stop: Not riding was driving her crazy. She knew riding was more important to her than anything else.

Julie had other struggles as well. Shortly after she became fully licensed as a jockey, the filly she was riding stumbled while leaving the starting gate, and both horse and rider went down. The filly rolled over Julie, breaking her back. Fortunately, there was no lasting damage. The doctor told her to take three months off, but after a month she was riding again, wearing a brace.

Then, in 1989, a three-year-old mount spooked at a shadow on the track, and she went flying over his head. He stepped on her and the horse behind him stepped on her, breaking her arm in four places, dislocating her shoulder, and giving her a concussion. This time it took eight months to heal.

In 1993, six weeks after the Belmont Stakes, during the last race of the season at Saratoga Springs in New York, her horse and another tangled hooves. Julie was knocked off; she landed first on her right foot, then bounced into a seated position in front of the oncoming pack of 1,100-pound horses traveling at thirty-five miles an hour. A horse named Two Is Trouble kicked her in the chest.

Julie's two-pound safety vest saved her life. Her ankle was shattered, her elbow punctured with joint damage, and she had a bruise on her heart. She had to have two surgeries on her ankle; it was repaired with two metal plates and fourteen screws. The injury and the recovery caused her an enormous amount of pain. "The skin on my ankle had been bandaged for so long that even the air hurt,"

Julie writes. "It was humiliating for me. I've always been strong and able to take care of myself." Instead, it took her eight months, with assistance from a team of doctors and therapists and friends, to get back on her feet.

Her will drove her back. Yet in early 1995, she had another bad fall at Gulfstream Park in Florida. She broke bones in her fingers and hands. This time something snapped in her mind, too. The injury was not physically as bad as the previous one, but it damaged her confidence. Julie had gotten spooked.

"Horses felt my anxiety, they got weird, they reared up," she told *The New York Times*. "I had been given a magical talent. I could pick a horse up with my will and put it right down in front. And then suddenly it was all gone."

There's no question that horse racing is dangerous. A University of North Carolina study of jockey accidents from 1993 to 1996 confirmed this fact—something everyone at the track already knows. The study documented 6,545 serious injuries among 2,700 jockeys during that period—that's about two and a half accidents per jockey, or almost one a year for every rider. And that's just the most serious injuries.

Julie had always been the comeback kid. But now she was losing. She no longer felt confident riding the inside track, slipping through impossible holes. Jockeys said she'd gotten chicken. Trainers she'd worked with for years took her off their top mounts. Julie was depressed. She had lost her love for racing.

"The only real relief I felt was planning my suicide. I saved sleeping pills, but I was going to drink alcohol, slit my wrists, and maybe hang myself, too. I wanted to do one thing right," she told *The New York Times*.

When a friend, a race fan and psychiatrist, ran into her at the track and heard her depressed comment that "there might not be a tomorrow," he suggested she come to his office for a talk. She began psychotherapy and eventually started taking antidepressants. She was diagnosed with post-traumatic stress disorder from her falls. She says the therapy eventually brought her back to herself.

"You don't fully realize how weird it was until you have yourself back," she said after she started riding again in 1997. She raced for another two years and had a good number of wins. She was having fun again. But in April 1999, she announced her retirement. Julie said at the time, "I don't want to get hurt anymore and I've got nothing left to prove." She left the sport with 3,545 wins—the most by far of any woman jockey—and $81 million in purses. She ranked sixteenth in career earnings.

But it was not an easy time. Her four-year marriage to television journalist Matt Muzikar was falling apart. Her mother was sick. Judi Krone had battled cancer in the 1980s; back then, her daughter had done her best to take care of her. At that time, Judi had gotten a new foal, Peter Rabbit, and her daughter said, "You can't die now, because you have to train that foal to be a jumper for me." It took two years of difficult treatments, but Judi had recovered. She'd spent a lot of her time training her new foal.

Now, thirteen years later, the cancer was back. Her daughter sold her farm in New Jersey and relocated to Florida to take care of her mother. Julie credits her mom with introducing her to the world of horses; it was Judi who taught her an intuitive, natural way of working with the animals. "You had to learn how to make the horses want to be with you. You couldn't just tie them up and have them do all the things with their ears pinned back. You had to get horses to trust and love you, and all the other things. My mom showed me that," she wrote in her memoir.

Judi Krone died in December that year, at the age of fifty-eight. Retired, unsure of her next step, Julie moved to Southern California with Peter Rabbit, the jumper her mother had trained. She began working as a commentator for a cable horse-racing channel and helped trainers exercise their horses. Her divorce finalized, she started to build a new life.

And then she met Jay Hovdey, a *Daily Racing Form* columnist whose writing she'd known for years. Jay was doing a profile on Julie, a where-is-she-now piece a year after her retirement. "I had an instant crush on him," she says. "I liked his personality. He made me laugh. About a month later we went out on our first date, and we were never apart after that."

The newlyweds moved to the town of Carlsbad, not far from the Del Mar Racetrack. Julie's depression had lifted. She was in a new relationship and was finding happiness in her new life. She was settled and felt better than she had in a long while. And a thought began to nag at her: Maybe she should go back to racing.

It wasn't long before she gave in to that thought. Julie returned to the track in November 2002. She was thirty-nine years old and had been away for three and a half years. She had set herself up with some long odds: She was jumping back into a hard-living sport at an age when most athletes retire; she had a slew of old injuries; she was three years out of the saddle; and she was dropping into an entirely new environment in California.

But over the course of her career, Julie had become very familiar with longshots. She did what she'd always done so well. She waited for her moment. And when it was least expected, she leaped ahead on the homestretch for surprise glory.

That year Julie had twenty wins, to finish the year on 133 mounts. Jay Hovdey saw his wife at her happiest. "When I saw her coming back covered with mud and this smile on her face, I just started laughing. I understood how much fun this game brings her," he told *The New York Times* after her second victory post-comeback.

The next year she finished second in the Del Mar standings, with forty-nine wins in forty-three days.

And Julie added to her storybook records by becoming the first woman to win a Breeders' Cup flat race on Halfbridled at Santa Anita, coming from a difficult outside post position to win the field of fourteen with a $917,000 purse. After this win, Jay says, he was "sobbing like a baby." He knew how hard she had worked to return to racing. She deserved the recognition, and "looked freaking glorious" on her victory ride, he says.

It couldn't last. Julie knew enough about timing to know that: The homestretch always comes to an end. She had some sore spots that continued to plague her. And it got harder to recover from fresh injuries. "As you get older, you start limiting your physical options," she says. "Your body changes. The physical consequences of being an athlete rear their ugly heads."

After a fall that winter, she never felt right. Julie stopped riding in February 2004. She refused to say she was retiring, because she said she'd "never say never." "I had a whirlwind tour of California racing," she said. "I had a lot of fun."

Now she's searching for a new role. "I've been a little bit lost for a little while. I'm so used to being so passionate and so intense. I was a jockey for twenty years; it's a hard habit to break. Every single day I'm sorting it out. I'm never at ease not riding races. I'm trying to find something that will take me away emotionally."

She continues to work on her horsemanship skills. After so much time on horses, a quest to improve might seem surprising, but Julie says she always has more to learn. "Humbleness goes along with the experience of spending your life with horses," she says. She's been training at a natural horsemanship program in Colorado and California. "It's kind of Zen-y," she says. "But you know what? I've become a better person because of this."

And Julie had a baby girl in September 2005, Lorelei Judith. Julie says she looks forward to sharing her love of horses with her daughter. "I don't care what she does, though," Julie says. "I'm going to wait and see what kind of person she is. I'll see what she needs to hear. I'm going to ride the horse that shows up. I just want her to look at me and say, 'Mom, I want to do this sooo bad,' whatever it is."

Seeing Beyond the Ball

Julie Foudy

Soccer Player Julie Foudy

Seventeen-year veteran of the U.S. national women's soccer team, with 230 international appearances; gold medal Atlanta Olympics 2004; third place World Cup 2003 (Carson, California); captain of San Diego Spirit 2001–2003; president, Women's Sports Foundation, 2000–2002; silver medal Sydney Olympics 2000; first place World Cup 1999 (Pasadena, California); gold medal Athens Olympics 1996; third place World Cup 1995 (Gävle, Sweden); first place World Cup 1991 (Guangzhou, China).

The victory of the U.S. women's soccer team in the 1999 World Cup was larger than sport. It was a watershed moment in American culture, and it was magical: Defender Brandi Chastain's game-winning penalty kick blasted into the goal's net and shattered perceived limits on what was possible in women's sports. It inspired a generation of girls to join soccer teams, delighted the country, and vindicated the efforts of the many women who had refused to be treated as second-class athletes.

The final match at the Rose Bowl in Pasadena had been a hot, scoreless game against China; world-class defense by both teams had driven the match into overtime and then into a penalty shoot-out.

Few players like the high-pressure, cruelly reductive finality of the shoot-out. Teams are allotted five kicks each, alternating, from twelve yards in front of the box, with only the opposing team's goalkeeper on hand to block the kick. Delivering a shot that is powerful and well-placed enough to get past the keeper into a net the size of a two-car garage is not physically difficult, but it is the pressure of the moment—the audience roaring, the keeper glaring and trying to intimidate the shooter, the game's conclusion resting on a single athlete's actions—that makes it terrifying. Nevertheless, most of the time penalty kicks are successful; if both teams make all of their shots and the score becomes tied at 5–5, then a sudden-death shoot-out phase begins.

Americans Carla Overbeck and Joy Fawcett made the first two shots for the U.S. team; the Chinese kickers were successful, too. For China's third shot, midfielder Liu Ying sent the ball left, but keeper Briana Scurry got a jump on it; her horizontal two-handed dive was a fantastic block. The U.S. team moved ahead by one. After Kristine Lilly and Mia Hamm's solid shots, plus two successful Chinese kicks, it all came down to the fifth kicker: Brandi Chastain.

Watching her from midfield was longtime teammate Julie Foudy (rhymes with "rowdy"), kicker number six. If Brandi missed, the American advantage would be gone. Midfielder Julie would be next. They would then be in a sudden-death situation. And the pressure would be all on her shoulders.

Along with Julie, eight other players lined up at midfield, with all eyes on Chastain. They had their arms around each other; as a group they bent forward in anticipation. Nerves etched lines across Julie's forehead. She squinted her blue eyes. Right then, she recollects, "I was just thinking, okay, let's get this over with."

Julie had played every moment of the 110 minutes of the final game. It was 105 degrees that afternoon. Everyone on the team was exhausted. But with their championship destiny about to unfurl in front of them, they were too focused to feel it.

Then came the kick, a rocket off Chastain's weaker foot, her left, to the right-side net. She hit it so powerfully the keeper could only throw out her arms. It was good. The women had done it—they had won the World Cup. Chastain dropped to her knees. The Americans at midfield raced forward. An image from that day sums it up: In the foreground is a soccer ball, having come to rest by the left post; midway back in the frame is Chastain on her knees, arched backward, arms to the sky in a pose of supplication—though at this point she's made simply of joy and muscle in a black sports bra, clutching her white shirt in her right fist; behind her, a semicircle of teammates sprints forward, arms raised, an exuberant swarm of team spirit and victory.

The image captures the exultancy of that perfect moment. The crowd roared; sparkling confetti dropped onto the field. It was a dramatic victory on home turf, and it was a tipping point for women's sports. The game was the best-attended women's sporting event ever, with 90,185 fans in the Rose Bowl. Little girls and boys wore Mia Hamm's number 9 jersey in solidarity; girls had their faces painted red, white, and blue; a teenage boy held a sign that read SOCCER BABES RULE! The parking lot had filled at eight o'clock that morning, five hours before the game. President Clinton and California governor Gray Davis were in the audience.

"America absolutely fell in love with this team," says Tony DiCicco, the World Cup head coach who also led the team at the 1995 World Cup and the 1996 Olympics. "They played soccer the way Americans want games to be played—they were very fair, very resourceful players; they were players that found a way to win."

It's surprising in retrospect that the team had struggled to convince event officials that women could draw audiences in large numbers. "We kept saying, just wait and see. The country will react," Julie says. And the public proved the team right: More than 650,000 people attended the World Cup series. Forty million viewers tuned in to the final on television. After the victory, the photograph of Chastain kneeling in celebration was on the front page of *Sports Illustrated, Time,* and *Newsweek,* as well as dozens of newspapers across the country.

The image of Chastain is the most memorable from the day, not only for the moment of joy it captured but for the odd and enduring sports-bra conversation it sparked—one that usually managed to combine prudishness, sexism, ignorance about soccer, and conspiracy theory paranoia (charges ranged from protestations that Chastain's image was indecent to allegations that she had planned her skin-baring moves and that Nike had paid her for her actions). But it was Scurry's save that was arguably the most crucial play. And this was a group of players who constantly emphasized their team effort. During the Cup, many members of the media tried to cast Mia Hamm as the team's star. With superb ball-handling skills and scoring ability, Hamm was certainly the player with the most finesse. But in every interview she made a point of mentioning the achievements of her teammates, the group undertaking of any victory, and the team's camaraderie.

Yet it is fair to say that the unprecedented phenomenon of the World Cup, including the public's enchantment with women's sports at a level never seen before, would not have been possible without the efforts of midfielder Julie Foudy.

Julie was one of those players who makes things happen; to use a common sports term, she was a playmaker. The team's cocaptain, Julie was a quick thinker on the field and was a natural leader. She understood the game and its players. And off the pitch, from early on, Julie was an outspoken, effective advocate for the sport. She not only performed exceptionally well at the World Cup, but through her leadership and vision, she was instrumental in building the tournament's national stage.

"What endears Julie to her teammates and her fans, and what makes her successful in the boardroom, is that she has a personality that brings people in," says Chastain. "She's very, very bright. She's also very quick to smile and to laugh and to make people feel at ease."

Julie played most of the World Cup games in 1999, taking a break in the third match, against North Korea, because DiCicco wanted to give his starters a rest. As a midfielder, Julie's job was to run the field, distribute the ball, and control the tempo of the game. Unlike American football's stops and starts, soccer is a continuously flowing game, requiring players to think quickly on their feet. Midfielders have to be nimble, switching from defense to offense as needed. "She has the ability to see the field, to play a few passes ahead of people," says Ian Sawyers, Julie's husband and the former coach of the women's pro-league team San Jose CyberRays.

With her well-balanced skills and her adaptability, Julie was a natural for the position. Midfielders are often team leaders. Though they aren't usually the ones to score or make saves, they are the driving force behind most of what happens on the field. They are the game's engine, not in a position of glamour but in one of leadership.

At five feet six, Julie was not one of the biggest players, nor was she one of the fastest, but she was graceful and confident. "She was our player of continual movement, always cruising—like a shark in water," says DiCicco. "She invented runs that I'm teaching today." According to teammate Chastain, Julie never lets up. "Everyone knows she's very verbal and outspoken, but she also leads by her actions. She does everything to the fullest," says Chastain. Julie owned the field, seeming to zip everywhere, her brown ponytail flapping, her partly opened mouth showing her tongue jammed against her teeth. That is, when she wasn't yelling out comments and directions to her teammates.

By the 1999 World Cup final, Julie, then twenty-eight, had played with the U.S. national women's team for twelve years. She had made key plays on their path to the Cup and in their past victories. In the opening game against Denmark, Julie scored the second goal with her left foot off a pass from Hamm. For the semifinal match against Brazil, Julie's shot in the fifth minute bounced off the Brazilian goalkeeper to teammate Cindy Parlow, who headed it in for a goal, giving the U.S. team an early lead and a psychological step up. They triumphed 2–0. Julie gave her teammates three assists in the tournament.

In 1998, in a lead-up tournament to the World Cup, Julie scored three goals against Ukraine on a freakishly cold day in Fresno, California, to lead the team's win. In the 1996 Olympics, which was the debut of women's soccer in the Games, it was her perfect pass, skirting a defender, to Shannon MacMillan in overtime in the semifinals against Norway that led them to victory; in the final, they triumphed over China for the gold medal

DiCicco sums it up simply: "She's a winner. We just needed her on the field."

Julie was also the team's laugh track, a playmaker for comedy. She was the one who had a joke for every situation. In fact, her pranks became part of team legend. In 1996, she conspired with coach DiCicco to forge an official-looking letter to Chastain announcing she would not be able to leave practice early in order to get to her own wedding. Chastain fumed until Julie, delighted, let her in on the joke. But at a team photo shoot, Chastain got her back. All but Julie lined up in jackets; underneath they wore T-shirts Chastain had made covered with a blown-up image of a younger, bushy-browed Julie and the phrase GOT TWEEZERS? across the front.

Totally unaware of the prank, Julie stepped to the middle, gazing at the photographer as the rest of the women took off their jackets and the joke was recorded on film. "Julie laughed hysterically," Chastain says. "That's another great thing about her: She can dish it out, and she can take it."

In the overtime of that World Cup final game, China came close to making a goal from a corner kick. Midfielder Kristine Lilly, in perfect position, headed it out from almost behind the post, and a definitive bicycle kick by Chastain sent the ball downfield. But the team was rattled—they'd come frighteningly close to losing the match. Julie broke the tension. "She just started laughing," DiCicco says. "She said, 'There's no way we're going to lose the game after that.' She's able to release tension with a laugh or a joke. That's great—and to be able to do it on the field is really special."

Julie was the kind of leader who came up with a nickname for every player. Chastain, because of her flair for the dramatic, was "Hollywood." Hamm was "Booter." And in return, teammates called her "Loudy Foudy." She earned it.

Julie has never been afraid of speaking up. "I've always been blessed with great vocal cords," she says. "I've never been shy. I assumed leadership roles early. I had confidence early on. I think that's probably a little abnormal for a lot of girls. But I think it had to do with sports, from all those lessons I learned on the field."

She grew up in Southern California's Mission Viejo, about sixty miles north of San Diego, and played football, soccer, baseball, basketball, and tennis with her two older brothers and older sister. "I tried everything growing up. I loved being outside," she says. In high school, she played on three soccer teams: her school's, as well as a regional team and an Olympic development team. But her focus on soccer, she says, didn't really start until college. In high school, she also played volleyball and ran track.

"She stood out immediately," says husband Ian, a longtime coach who first saw Julie play for a club team in the late 1980s. "She had the ability to change the tempo of the game. She was an attacking force. She could have an impact on the game at whatever level she was playing at."

At age sixteen, while playing with the national nineteen-and-under team, Julie caught the eye of Anson Dorrance, who was coaching the top-ranked University of North Carolina women's team. Dorrance invited her to join the national team. She traveled with them, and with fellow teenagers Mia Hamm and Kristine Lilly, for the first time in 1987 and played for them the following year. She missed her high school graduation in order to attend a national team match in Italy—something she says she regrets a bit. (Four years later, she skipped a game to attend her college graduation.)

Stanford was her choice for college, though the school's soccer program under coach Berhane Andeberhan was not yet a powerhouse. Julie turned down a full ride at the University of North Carolina, home of Dorrance's team, which was number one, because she wanted to remain in California; she was thinking about academics, too. And she was instrumental in building the Stanford team into a top program. By her senior year, Stanford was offering women full soccer scholarships for the first time.

At Stanford, Julie juggled premed classes, collegiate soccer, and the national team. She was named All American all four years, and was the 1991 Soccer America player of the year. School vacations were spent traveling the world with the team while studying on buses and trains. When the national team's season ended, she dove into playing for the NCAA. She was also dating women's soccer coach Ian Sawyers, who would later become her husband. Julie amazed her family and teammates with her ability to balance enormous amounts of responsibility and activity.

"She has a super amount of energy," says Ian. "Today, her idea of relaxing is to juggle four things at once. She'll water the plants and do fifteen jobs with her headset on. She's the ultimate multitasker."

By the close of the 1980s, the women's national team was already emerging as a global leader. But the incipient team had little funding from the sport's governing body, the U.S. Soccer Federation; players received no salaries and were given only a $10-per-day meal stipend during tournaments. Most of the games were played outside the country; events in the States were poorly attended. To get to matches, the team traveled on cargo planes (one time it took forty-five hours to arrive at their destination in Italy) and once on a sooty Bulgarian coal train. In Italy, they practiced on a gravel field. In 1990, for a tournament in China, they stayed at a hotel that offered hot water and electricity for only an hour a day.

"There was no way a men's team or even a youth team would stay in these places," Julie said in an interview for the HBO women's soccer movie *Dare to Dream*. "There was no recognition or interest on the women's side, it seemed. We'd get maybe a few hundred people out for the games, and there wasn't a lot of corporate support or sponsors or marketing. I remember when we got to keep our first USA jackets, a little blue-and-red windbreaker, and I was ecstatic. It was a very different world back then."

When the team won the inaugural 1991 Women's Cup, played in China, only three reporters met the champion team's homecoming plane. Few people in the States seemed to know there had even been a women's World Cup. Julie went immediately from the tournament back to school, to dive into final exams.

After graduation in 1993, Julie was a bit uncertain about what to do. Without a women's pro league in the United States, she didn't have a program to keep her skills sharp year-round, in between national team matches. So she went to play in a pro league in Sweden for a season. She debated becoming a doctor; she'd been accepted to Stanford Medical School. Her mother, a nurse, was encouraging. But "I just wasn't convinced I wanted to be a doctor," she says.

In 1994, a conversation with tennis great Billie Jean King at a sports roundtable event was a turning point for Julie. The players on the national team were still earning very little money, only a few thousand dollars a year. And with an increasing number of games on the schedule, they were traveling more and more. "We were gone all the time, so players couldn't hold down a second job," Julie says. "We had a laundry list of things that were issues. I was telling Billie Jean King that we'd been trying to get our federation to pay attention to these things for so long. And she said, '*Hello?!* Of course they're not going to do anything. There's no incentive for them to change. They're profiting. You've got to do something yourselves. Tell them you're not going to stand for this. Point out why it's not equitable. You guys have to *make* it happen.'"

King had led the effort to create the first women's tour in tennis in 1971 after being frustrated by the smaller prizes and condescending treatment of the women's matches. She was criticized at the time, but her actions led to what became the Virginia Slims tour, and tennis today is one of the rare sports in which women athletes receive equal prizes and acclaim. And King became the first female tennis player to make more than $100,000 in prize money in a year.

The conversation was an epiphany for Julie. The national team had an upcoming contract-signing meeting. Julie went back to her team and said, "We're not signing the contracts, and here's why." They agreed to stand as a team, refusing to sign until the federation agreed to pay them better. And when federation officials realized they had no choice, they agreed to improve salaries.

By insisting that the U.S. Soccer Federation take them seriously, the women laid the foundation for a team that the world would have to take seriously. Without having to juggle full-time employment, the players could focus on being the best athletes possible. This set in motion the journey to better treatment, better arenas, more lucrative sponsorship opportunities, and the outpouring of enthusiasm during the World Cup.

The successful contract negotiations in 1994 strengthened the team's bond. They returned to practice focused on the 1995 World Cup, which took place in Sweden. They started off strong: Julie scored a header goal in an early match against Australia, contributing to a 4–1 win. They beat Japan soundly, 4–0, and faced Norway in the semifinal. The Norwegians were a powerful team. They went on attack immediately, scoring in the tenth minute of the game. Despite many fierce efforts and two crossbar shots, the Americans weren't able to score for the next eighty minutes. The team watched the Norwegians celebrate by dancing on the field. They were devastated. They finished in third place, beating China in the consolation final.

But they knew how to bounce back. They regrouped, returning to training with a focus on winning at the next year's Olympics, where women's soccer would debut as a medal event. But a few months beforehand, the U.S. Soccer Federation told the team they would get a bonus only if they won a gold medal.

The men's team, which was not as strong internationally, would be awarded a bonus if they earned any medal—gold, silver, or bronze. Julie again saw this as unfair, and organized a boycott. Leading veteran players stood by her, including Michelle Akers, Kristine Lilly, Mia Hamm, and Tisha Venturini. They refused to play until the federation dealt with the women's team equally. The federation thought they would break after a short time and it brought in new players. But after weeks without their stars at practice, the organization backed down. They agreed to give the women bonuses for any medal.

One good thing that came out of the strike was the reemergence of Brandi Chastain. She'd been left off the 1995 World Cup team; the coaches thought she wasn't fit enough. When she got the chance to play during the strike, she wowed the team; she ran drills, she was in great shape, and her skills were strong. With the strike over, Julie and the others came back to a team that now included Chastain as its newest member.

And the whole medal debate turned out to be moot, since the women's team won the gold, beating China 2–1. But again, they had sent a message: We want equal treatment. We demand respect.

It was an ongoing battle. During the Olympics, NBC decided not to televise the women's final game, assuming interest in the women's team wasn't great enough to merit the ninety minutes of airtime. So Americans couldn't watch the women win the gold medal; they saw only highlights. Nevertheless, despite NBC's vote of no confidence, the gold medal win solidified the importance of women's soccer. Commentators called the 1996 Games in Atlanta the "Summer of Women"; the women's basketball, gymnastics, and softball teams earned gold along with the soccer team. U.S. Olympic Committee Executive Director Dick Schultz said at the time, "These games have belonged to the women. They've given girls around the world athletic role models." Kristine Lilly noted, "The fans saw women for the first time as athletes who loved competing for no other reason than to have fun and win and not for money or glory, and I think that kind of swept the country."

Julie and her teammates planned to ride the tide of support into the 1999 World Cup. Seven players from the 1991 team were returning. They were an outstanding bunch: strong, mature, skilled, and exciting to watch. They were ranked number one. And this Cup would be played in the United States. Julie understood they had a special opportunity to show Americans on a grand scale what women athletes could do.

But at first the U.S. Soccer Federation didn't have the same vision. Organizers initially planned to stage the matches in small stadiums, with five thousand to six thousand seats. The cost of large stadiums was a concern. And they didn't want television cameras to pan across large sections of empty seats.

But one official who didn't agree was World Cup President Marla Messing; she pushed for the larger arenas. "Once you decide on five thousand or ten thousand seats, the image of what you are selling is second-class," she told Jere Longman for his excellent book, *The Girls of Summer: The U.S. Women's Soccer Team and How It Changed the World.*

Messing enlisted the team to promote the event in unconventional ways, with articles in *Seventeen* magazine and *Teen People.* Chastain got a lot of attention after a photo of her posing with only a couple of soccer balls for modesty appeared in *Gear* magazine (a step tamer than 1970s keeper and centerfold Shep Messing (no relation to Marla), who famously posed full frontal for a woman's magazine in 1974). She was also invited to appear on David Letterman's show, where she charmed him so much that his jokes about the team he called "Babe City" were part of his nightly routine during the tournament.

"So many people were so negative about us playing in big stadiums," says Julie. "We did a lot of grassroots work, we had a really concentrated effort on the marketing side. Then to walk into the Rose Bowl, just packed—it shows you."

After the World Cup win, the country was in love with women's soccer. And Julie and teammates knew the opportunity to build the sport should not be missed. Buoyed by support from Disney Channel Founder John Hendricks, Julie and others pushed to form a pro league, the Women's United Soccer Association (WUSA). Top players from China, Norway, Germany, France, Canada, and Brazil were recruited. Hendricks became the chairman.

The eight-team league debuted in 2001 with a season of twenty-one games. Julie became a voting player representative on the WUSA governing board. Remembering her struggles a decade earlier, Julie negotiated aggressively for decent salaries, particularly for the incoming, lowest-paid players. The pay scale ranged from $25,000 to $85,000. "I think that's rare in a professional sports environment," says Chastain. "Julie spoke up for the players who were at the bottom of the pay scale. She had been around; as one of the oldest players, she deserved to be paid more. But she was never self-important. The national team was a very inclusive group. Because of that, many younger players had a chance to be pro athletes."

Julie played for the San Diego Spirit, close to her hometown, and was the team captain. "She was the only player in sports history to be on the board of governors in a pro sports league," says DiCicco, who was the WUSA's commissioner.

Attendance averaged close to seven thousand spectators a game. But though the league was funded in large part by cable TV companies, the ratings were minuscule, drawing just a fraction of a percent of households. And after 9/11, the economy took a sharp downturn; corporate sponsors withdrew promised funding. Five days before the opening match of the 2003 Women's World Cup, after only three seasons, the WUSA shut down, claiming $50 million in losses.

As the players' representative, Julie had to make the announcement to them. "I was heartbroken," she says. "I really thought our product was great. The fan base was good. But we had some investors not willing to stomach some of the losses."

Julie believed in the power of sports. She wanted to make it easier for girls in the next generation. "I think it's good for young kids, not just girls but boys, too, to be watching women do these things on the field; it's good for them to not just see professional male athletes. That saddens me that now they don't have that on a weekly basis."

While playing for the San Diego Spirit, Julie also served as president of the Women's Sports Foundation, headquartered in New York, and was appointed to the Presidential Commission on Title IX, the 1972 equal opportunity law.

The commission's goal was to make recommendations on several proposals to change the details of Title IX. The landmark legislation had guaranteed equal access to programs for girls and women at federally funded institutions and had most often been applied to sports programs. But the proposals would weaken the application of its mandates, including widening the margin by which a school could acceptably fail to fund women's programs in proportion to its female population and requiring female athletes to prove sufficient interest in a sport for funding (instead of relying on population numbers for proportionate funding requirements).

Julie did an enormous amount of research. When committee members said they were supporting changes to the law, Julie, with fellow commission member and Olympic swimmer Donna de Varona, refused to sign. They didn't support weakening Title IX in any way. They issued a minority report and generated publicity. When the public became aware of what was at stake, support was overwhelmingly with Julie and Donna.

In the end, because of the bad press, the committee recommended making no changes to Title IX in 2003. Dawn Riley, who became president of the Women's Sports Foundation after Julie, publicly thanked Julie and Donna. "Their courage in communicating the facts that should have guided the commission's work resulted in a media and public debate," she said.

Julie's vision, this time off the field, helped secure future opportunities for women athletes.

Julie, at age thirty-three, played her final competitive match in the 2004 Olympics. For a time beforehand, it looked like she might not be able to. In the sixtieth minute of the semifinal, against the German team, a defender accidentally wrenched Julie's ankle. She couldn't walk and had to come out of the game. The final was in two days. She had never missed a game because of injury. And now she might have to sit out the last match of her career.

"It wasn't the easiest year," says Ian. "She managed to pull it together as a captain and leader. This was her final game and it looked like she was going to miss it."

But Julie rested and willed herself better. She played every minute of that last game, the last time she'd play in a competitive match with Hamm, Lilly, Fawcett, Chastain, and Scurry. Brazil played aggressively, even scrappily—American commentators thought the team got away with too many fouls. But it didn't matter: The U.S. team won 2–1, with goals by members of the next generation of American stars: Abby Wambach and Lindsay Tarpley. And Julie won her second Olympic gold medal.

"That was awesome, to see her overcome all the stuff, to finish her career on a high. That was a really proud moment," says Ian.

Julie retired after the Olympics, though she played in a few victory tour games. She says she doesn't miss playing. Last year, she and her husband started the Julie Foudy Sports Leadership Academy, a soccer camp program that also teaches girls leadership skills. She worked as a commentator for ESPN during the 2006 men's World Cup—a rare female analyst in the sports broadcast booth. And she's working, optimistically, to resurrect the women's pro league—for the next generation, including her daughter, Isabel Sawyers, born in 2007. On and off the field, Julie never gives up.

And she inspires others to keep going, too. Marlene Bjornsrud, former general manager of the San Jose CyberRays, was ready to throw in the towel after the pro league folded. She had devoted her career to women's sports, coaching at Santa Clara University before working for the CyberRays, but now she thought she'd find something more secure.

"You know what, I'm tired," she says she told Julie. "We've got to leave this to the next generation. But Julie said 'No, you can't do that. They don't appreciate Title IX. Let's do something, let's continue the journey.'"

Julie, Bjornsrud, and Chastain formed the Bay Area Women's Sports Initiative, or BAWSI (pronounced "bossy," which is "the perfect name," Chastain says). The program offers coaching and classes to schoolgirls, elementary to high school, who have lacked sports opportunities. Bjornsrud says, "Julie's mantra, a phrase she uses all the time, is 'Choose to Matter.' That's the spirit of BAWSI. When Julie said that, I thought, *Okay. We'll do it.* College-age athletes may not understand Title IX, but they can understand that we owe it to our community to choose to matter."

From its beginnings in 2005, the group has grown thirtyfold. The first class had twenty girls; today the program reaches more than six hundred and has added workouts for the girls' mothers, as well. More than sixty women athletes from Santa Clara and San Jose State Universities are coaching and teaching in the program.

Bjornsrud says she wouldn't have had the energy to get involved if not for Julie. "In my book, she is it. Her skills of getting people to work together, to be on the same page for a cause or for a game, those skills are extraordinary. I don't think there's anyone else out there like her."

National Hope

Deena Kastor

═══ Runner
Deena Kastor

Winner of Flora London Marathon 2006 (2:19:36, an American record); second place in Berlin half-marathon 2006 (1:07:34, an American record); winner of LaSalle Bank Chicago Marathon 2005 (2:21:25); bronze medal in Olympic marathon 2004 (2:27:20).

At marathoner Deena Drossin Kastor's home in Oxnard, California, about fifty miles northwest of Los Angeles, a soft green-and-red painting of a woman's lower legs hangs in one of the extra bedrooms. It's an appealing image: The woman is wearing flip-flops, her toenails are colorfully painted, and her ankles are casually crossed as she stands with her weight on one leg. Its mood suits the Kastors' new casual and comfortable two-story house, located a short jog from the beach. I compliment the painting and Deena, the country's fastest female distance runner, ducks her head, almost shyly.

"I painted that," she says. "I love feet. I'm obsessed. Of course, mine never look that good."

An obsession with feet is surely understandable for a woman who has used her own to break national records for speed. And it's no wonder that they'd be a bit rough around the edges. With her 2006 win at the London Marathon, Deena set a new U.S. record for the 26.2-mile distance, finishing in two hours, nineteen minutes, and thirty-six seconds. She bested her own time from the London race three years prior, when she became the first American woman in seventeen years to surpass Joan Benoit Samuelson's Chicago Marathon time.

Deena offers relief to the long drought in American women's distance running. Since Samuelson's triumphs during the 1980s, U.S. distance women have not excelled in international competition. (The men, too, have receded from the international stage since the days of Alberto Salazar, but many hopes are pinned on Deena's fellow Californian, Meb Keflezighi, who won the 2004 silver medal in the Olympics.) Norwegians Grete Waitz and Ingrid Kristiansen, Portuguese Rosa Mota, and Kenyan Tegla Loroupe dominated the 1990s as Samuelson faced setbacks due to injuries in the late '80s; since 2001, Brit Paula Radcliffe has been the leading record setter, with contingents from Kenya, Romania, Japan, and China battling it out behind her. During this time, American women have largely been absent from the top spots. Deena's bronze medal in the 2004 Olympics was the first U.S. women's distance-running medal since Samuelson's gold twenty years prior, and her Chicago win in 2005 was the first major marathon win by an American woman on U.S. soil in eleven years.

It doesn't take a lot of equipment to become a runner. In that sense, the sport might provide the world's most level playing field. An aspiring runner is likely to get further relying purely on talent and will than athletes in sports requiring fancy equipment and skilled teammates. "Running is perhaps the most fundamental of all sports, and it is economically the least costly to perform," writes runner and naturalist Bernd Heinrich in *Why We Run*. "As a result, it is the most democractic and the most competitive." There's no reason Americans should expect to stand out on the global stage. Except . . .

Except, no American runner who was inspired as a child by Samuelson's gold the first time women competed in the marathon in the Olympics, or who was gripped by Salazar and Dick Beardsley's New York City battle to the final steps in 1982, or who was overcome with melancholy wondering what University of Oregon star Steve Prefontaine might have raced to had he lived beyond the age of twenty-four—no one can say there hasn't been a trace of wistfulness pacing American competitors all these years.

Deena Kastor plans to change all that.

1. They always teach you something

Deena has strawberry blond hair, bright blue eyes, and pale freckles on her face and arms. Her chocolate lab, Aspen, follows her as she slides through the house in foam flip-flops. She has prepared an elegant plate of appetizers for us—hummus, cheese, and fruit. A pitcher of iced tea sweats on the marble countertop. She pours us each a glass. She is, not surprisingly, incredibly lean—her pumpkin-colored sweater seems like it might be too heavy for her arms; in her jean skirt, her legs look almost delicate—but of course Deena is anything but.

When she's training for a marathon, Deena logs about 130 miles a week. She starts her day with an intense run, takes an afternoon nap, and goes for an easy recovery run most evenings, usually accompanied partway by her dog. Deena trains with Team Running USA and, most of the time, goes through her paces above eight thousand feet near her home in Mammoth Lakes, a resort town on the eastern side of California's Sierra Nevada range. For sea level work, she goes to the Olympic training center in Chula Vista, near

San Diego. Two years ago, she and husband Andrew purchased this second home in Oxnard, which is closer to Deena's parents and the L.A. suburb where she grew up.

Deena's first love in sports was cross-country racing—running trail races—and she continues to compete in track and cross-country events. She likes the balance of switching between speed and distance work. She says it prevents a runner from getting stale. But the marathon is the big kahuna of distance running. It's where all the money and media attention resides. A great 10,000-meter runner gains fame in track circles, but a great marathoner will become a household name. In the buildup to last year's fall New York Marathon, Deena's image was on billboards and in subway trains all over the city; *The New York Times* ran a 1,300-word profile of her in its magazine, identifying her as the face of the race. It's hard to imagine a 10K event prompting the same kind of attention. "The marathon has a huge allure to people," says Terrence Mahon, Deena's coach. "To think there are women out there running at a five-minute-mile pace and under, to think they can hold that up for 26.2 miles when your average person couldn't do it for a quarter mile, it becomes awe-inspiring."

Marathoning is one of the few sports in which men and women generally get equal prize money. For the New York Marathon last year, both the men's and women's winner received $130,000, plus bonuses and awards. For winning London last year, Deena received $105,000, and she won $125,000 in Chicago. Celebrity runners also receive appearance fees for big races; in New York, Deena received more than $100,000 just for toeing the starting line.

As we settle in to snacks and drinks at her kitchen table, Deena says she sees every race as a lesson. "It seems like they always teach you something," she says. And marathons must provide the greatest teachings of all.

At her marathon debut, in New York at age twenty-eight, Deena placed seventh, after winner Margaret Okayo and second-place finisher Susan Chepkemei, both of Kenya, and third-place finisher Svetlana Zakharova of Russia. It was impressive for a first timer. She was only two minutes, thirty-seven seconds behind the leader and had the fastest debut of any American woman in history. Deena showed she was ready to be a world-class competitor.

2. It's what's in your head that makes the difference

Deena didn't immediately take to sports as a kid: She and her younger sister preferred games with Barbies over physical competition. "While all the kids were out playing on the street, I'd be over in my back yard, playing with my imaginary friends. I was always content to be by myself," she says. Her dad got her to try soccer when he signed up to be a coach, but she didn't excel. Next she tried softball, but, she says, "I was the kid out in left field, wearing a daisy chain. I think I let the ball roll by me once because I was trying to hook a necklace on."

Her parents suggested signing up for cross-country in middle school. They were worried that their oldest child spent too much time alone. Deena was lukewarm on the idea—until she tried it. "I loved it from the first day. Something clicked. It was a natural for me. It felt so good to just run," she says. She excelled at distance and stayed away from sprints, in part because an unbeatable teenage Marion Jones was racing for a rival club.

She liked the social aspect of the sport. Running with small groups on trails near her school, doing repeats and drills on the track surrounded by teammates—the experiences coaxed her out of her shell. And she was talented. Deena went on to win two state high school titles in track and three in cross-country and went to the national finals four times.

Deena believes in the power of verbalizing her goals. She learned early on that stating what she wanted to accomplish could help make it happen. Preparing for the London Marathon in 2003, two years after her marathon debut, Deena announced to the media that her goal was to break Samuelson's record time of 2:21:21 from 1985. It was a bold move. She was laying her ambition out for the public to judge.

The London race is a fast one; three of the five best times ever run by a woman marathoner have been run here. Deena started off great, on target and feeling strong. She was in the lead group, trailing Paula Radcliffe and Kenyan Catherine Ndereba. But with ten thousand meters remaining, she realized she wasn't at her hoped-for pace.

Ten thousand meters was the distance she'd always called her best. But it looked like she might not reach the goal she'd so boldly laid out. "I had some 10K splits marked down on my arm to give me some guidelines, and I was forty seconds off. Instantly, when I saw those numbers, my legs got heavy and I heard my feet slapping the pavement," she told a reporter from USA Track & Field afterward. "For about a half mile I was thinking, *I can't do this. I'm not on record pace.* Then I kind of woke myself up and out of it and said even if I don't get the record, I'm on pace for a huge personal best right now. I thought, *It's not worth it to give up this easily.*"

Her energy renewed, Deena sprinted to the finish for a third-place spot, breaking Samuelson's long-standing record by five seconds. "I think anyone will tell you that marathoning doesn't feel good. I guess you have good moments, but really it's a psychological battle," she said afterward. "The biggest lesson I walked away with was just how mental the sport of marathoning is."

3. Run your own race

The Razorbacks and Lady Razorbacks of the University of Arkansas between them have won more than forty national championship titles in cross-country and track and field. So the school was a logical choice for Deena's college career. As a student there, she was named All American in both cross-country and track, and her team won seven Southeastern Conference titles. But after her impressive high school showing, she felt she wasn't living up to her potential. She never dominated beyond the conference; after four years she lacked a national title. Her post-graduation coach, renowned running coach Joe Vigil, wrote afterward that "the outstanding talent she displayed as a high school runner was never realized in college."

Deena majored in creative writing and found she loved writing fiction and poetry. By the time she was a senior, she was still racing well, but her enthusiasm for running was waning. "I was writing with my friends in coffee shops, and I was thinking, *I will just do something else.* Since I'd been eleven years old, I'd been traveling and competing. And I'm interested in so many things."

After graduating, Deena imagined she might move to Boulder, Colorado, and open a bakery. "I have a passion for baking and cooking. I love entertaining," she says. "Cooking for people is a dream come true for me." She has a signature avocado enchilada recipe and another for eggplant polenta casserole. She fantasized about starting a small café—a place that would serve pastries and maybe some light meals.

The running blinders—the incredible focus that had gotten her so far—were now off. There were a lot of things out there, a whole world that Deena hadn't had time to explore before. She spent many weeks weighing her passion for running against her curiosity about everything else. *Okay, I need to analyze this,* she told herself, taking her typical rational approach to tackling problems.

She thought her way through the dilemma. After months of deliberating, she had a breakthrough. She wasn't ready to move on because she wasn't finished discovering what she could do. "I thought, *I can sit in cafés later. I can open a bakery at any age.* If I really wanted to see how I would run, what potential I would meet, I needed to run. I hadn't won any national championships in college because I didn't put my heart and soul in. If I was going to stop, I wanted it to be that I had given it my all. And I knew I could do more than I had."

Determined now, but uncertain what direction to take, Deena was encouraged by a college coach to telephone Joe Vigil, who was living at elevation in Alamosa, Colorado, about 260 miles southwest of Boulder. Coach Vigil has a doctorate in exercise physiology and takes a no-nonsense approach to training. He'd founded an outstanding cross-country program at the small local college, Adams State, and had coached in several Olympics.

"I clicked with him so well on the phone," Deena says. "He was a no-frills kind of guy. He emphasized motivation. And he was the most difficult coach in the country in terms of what he asked of his athletes. But he said I needed to take control of my training."

Vigil later said he'd been skeptical at first, but through the course of the phone conversation Deena's reaffirmed dedication to the sport convinced him. She moved to Alamosa, at 7,500 feet in elevation, to begin training. She got a job working the opening shift at a coffee shop four days a week. "It was just enough to allow me to get by and have time to practice," she says.

Vigil had her rest well and eat well. She noticed an improvement right away as soon as she started getting enough sleep—ten hours a night. Deena scaled her life back to the fundamentals: train, eat, work, and sleep. Coach Vigil had a three-year plan to boost her mileage, initially raising it from about fifty miles weekly to seventy. Adding miles and gradually increasing the intensity of Deena's tempo runs—shorter runs at a rapid pace—increased the maximum amount of oxygen her body could use in a minute (what athletes call the "VO_2 max"). After a little more than a year, Vigil raised her mileage to ninety miles a week.

"I got into a great routine; I saw results immediately," Deena says. In town, she met a physical therapist named Andrew Kastor. He'd been a competitive runner himself. He rode his bike to pace her on her long runs. Deena started to see competitive results—she won a championship in cross-country. Finally, she had her national title.

"Everything else fell into place then, immediately after college. I haven't had a down year since," Deena says. And she and Kastor were married in 2003.

In 2001, Vigil relocated his team to Mammoth Lakes in California, where runners could train at an even higher altitude than in Colorado. Coach Terrence Mahon joined the group when Vigil, in his sixties, took a step back from the daily intensity (though he remains an adviser to the team). In the fall of that year, Deena made her marathon debut in New York. And by 2004, she had qualified for the Olympic marathon team.

At Deena's first Olympic marathon (she'd run the 10k in Sydney in 2000 but didn't progress from the finals), everyone was worried about the heat. In Athens that day in August it was 102 degrees at six in the evening when the gun went off. The course into the city, a route that legend says killed Pheidippides in 490 BC, had long, draining hills and limited shade. A *New York Times* reporter called it "perhaps the most ruthless Olympic marathon course ever." All of the runners knew their biggest competitor that day was the heat. Deena had struggled earlier that year in the trials, placing second in St. Louis. But since then she'd adjusted her sports drinks and stepped up her elevation training. She'd been practicing in extra layers in the California mountains to simulate the Mediterranean's extreme summer. And she'd arrived in Greece three weeks early to give herself time to acclimate. She knew she performed well under a challenge: She actually likes racing in difficult conditions. "I feel like my body adjusts pretty well to whatever the conditions could bring. I would like it to be a little excruciating out there," she said before the race. She was ready.

The course opened with eight miles of hills, then gradually leveled off and ended with a descent. Deena started out slow; she was twelfth at the midway mark. As she knocked off the early hills, Deena felt strong. She increased her pace. It was getting pretty excruciating for all of the runners; everyone was drenched in sweat. With four miles to go, Radcliffe, the British world-record holder, staggered, then dropped to the side of the road. After a moment, she tried to start up again, took a few unsteady strides, and gave up. The top woman had just dropped out of the race. Opportunity widened; Deena began moving up in the field. Leaders Mizuki Noguchi of Japan and Ndereba of Kenya were a step apart, almost a minute ahead. Deena wasn't even sure where she was in the order. When she entered Panathinaiko Stadium, the announcer called Deena's third-place position and she burst into tears.

Commentators said Deena ran a strategically inspired race. Always a perfectionist, she immediately thought of ways she could have run better. "I should have picked up the pace. The lesson was that if time was the goal, running an even-paced race is the most efficient way to do it. Why was I so conservative for so long?" she asks herself.

4. Don't get distracted

The next year, Deena felt she was an even stronger runner. But her first marathon victory in Chicago, in 2005, was a painful one. The Windy City's flat course is a good one for records, and Deena hoped to break the 2:20 barrier—something that, at the time, fewer than a dozen women had done.

The leading group started out fast. Deena's training partner, Mike McKeeman, who ran as a pacesetter (hired by race organizers, pacesetters, or "rabbits," set a tempo and are contracted to drop out before the end) for the first twenty miles that day, said later it felt like they were collectively carried away by the moment. "Everyone got caught up, with all of the people, the excitement of the race," he says.

Deena was at a 2:18:32 pace at the halfway mark, much faster than she had ever run. Romanian Constantina Tomescu-Dita kept challenging her, matching her stride; at mile 18, Deena had had enough. She wanted to lose her. She pushed it, going really hard. By mile 20, she was running alone, the leader. But she'd gone faster than ever before—crossing mile 20, she was at what would be a 2:17 marathon—and it was too much. Two miles later, Deena hit a wall. She began to struggle, and slowed. Her legs stiffened. Tomescu-Dita, who'd been forty seconds behind, closed in. Deena was dehydrated and hurting worse than she ever had. Her pace dropped from less than 5:20 a mile to 6:15—that kind of marathon rate would earn her a marathon of 2:44, a respectable time for an age-grouper but far off a world-class pace.

"There wasn't anything that anybody could say to me to get me to move faster," she says. "Nothing. I couldn't drink more fluids, there was no magical motivating sentence. It was the hardest thing I've had to do. I could feel my body falling apart and I had no control over it. It was the worst feeling I've ever had."

She struggled to the line just five seconds ahead of Tomescu-Dita for a finish of 2:21:25. She won—"but not gracefully," she says. The victory was "bittersweet."

Deena's mistake had been to let the competition rattle her, says Coach Mahon. She hadn't controlled the pacing as she should have. "She was pushing too hard at some of the wrong times," Mahon says. "She was pushing in the beginning, in the middle of the race, at the start of the last third—she didn't need to do that. She had competition with her and was a little shocked, so she gave it a push. She got rid of the other woman, but a couple miles later, it was to her detriment. She needed to run her race the whole time, and let other people run their race."

It was a lesson she would remember.

5. Define excellence in your own terms

Deena likes to plan things out. She has the focused, structured thinking of a great distance runner. One of the techniques she learned from Coach Vigil is to break each race into segments, each training period into steps. At the start of each year, she sets her goals—high ones—and then maps out a way to reach them. She has some plans for the distant future, like having a child and opening that bakery. Others are in closer focus. For running, there's still a lot she wants to do. "I haven't hit my personal best yet. A bronze medal isn't good enough," she says.

She is careful and modest when evaluating the current field of competitive distance runners. At every occasion, she points out that there are many strong women racing today. The media has made a lot of a potential matchup between her and Radcliffe, who's been called unbeatable; but Radcliffe didn't compete for most of 2006, announcing that she was pregnant and would return to racing in the fall of 2007. Regardless, Deena refuses to focus on one competitor. "I don't think she's the only threat out there. There are too many great performances, so many women up and coming," she says.

This, she notes, is good for the sport. The women's field is dynamic. "Men have been doing it for so long, they're improving now by milliseconds. But women are breaking records by minutes, by twenty points. It's exciting to see the momentum women are creating—and it's going to continue," she says.

The new World Marathon Majors prize, launched for the first time for 2006 and 2007, highlights how global competition is heating up. The $1 million prize will be split between the top male and female point winners in a five-marathon contest over a two-year period. Deena is one of the top contenders.

In London in 2006, Deena put it all together. She raced against an excellent field, including her Chicago rival Tomescu-Dita, Russian Ludmila Petrova, and Kenyan Susan Chepkemei. She, Chepkemei, and Kenyan Salina Kosgei grabbed the lead from the outset. But this time Deena took command. She set her pace and steadily earned the lead. Kosgei dropped back at mile 10; Chepkemei fought to stay with Deena.

With three miles to go, Deena looked completely in control. She was running "absolutely fabulous," according to an observer riding in the lead vehicle. And Chepkemei was visibly struggling. But the Kenyan racer held on. "You do these little checks with people," Deena says. "Susan's breathing was labored. But she was still with me. And I had a moment of doubt. I thought: *Second place isn't* that *bad.* I know how tough she is. It was a moment of weakness." At the marble countertop in her kitchen, Deena waves her hands to show how she shoved the thought away.

Chepkemei held on. "She was still right there with me." *When am I going to shake her?* Deena wondered. "I was just wanting to get there. But I didn't want to take a risk on surging. You never know until you see that finish line." Deena stayed on pace as Chepkemei dropped back in the last mile; she won the race at 2:19:36. She set a new American record and accomplished her goal of breaking the 2:20 barrier. Hers was the eighth-fastest time in the world; she was the sixth-fastest woman. She ran a perfect race, her splits absolutely matched at 1:09:48 (race officials called her "metronomic"). And though she says she suffered in the last three miles, this was nothing like Chicago. She walked away easily, even gracefully.

And what did she learn from her London victory? She doesn't hesitate: "I can run faster than that," she says.

6. If it's not working, change your pace and change your plan
Coach Mahon calls Deena an incredibly smart athlete. The trinity of sports achievement, he says, is talent, dedication, and intelligence. And it's rare to find an athlete who excels in all three. But Deena does. Her talent has been evident since childhood. She's proven her dedication through the years. And, Mahon says, "She has a very good intelligence in learning what she can take. She's an intelligent racer. She knows to run her own race and not get swept into what other athletes are doing. She has made mistakes along the way and learned from them."

Deena has continued to compete in shorter races even as she pursues her marathon goals. Her first love was always cross-country. And she has set national records in both half-marathon distance races and 10,000-meter distances; no American woman before her has simultaneously held records in all these distances. (Frank Shorter and Alberto Salazar are the only men who held records in the marathon and the 10K.)

But last summer, she may have been overly ambitious. After her win at London, she had lined up races in Switzerland and Italy. She traveled to Belgium to train with her team and scaled back her weekly workout distance to focus on speed. But she just couldn't get her legs to move.

She did poorly in her initial 3,000-meter race and couldn't even run the next day because she was so sore. "What is happening to me?" she wrote in her training journal. "Things just aren't clicking."

"It was hard seeing Deena struggle like that," says training partner McKeeman. "It was the first time since I've been with her that she was going through some rough patches. It was odd to see her unable to just go out and do anything we told her to do."

Coach Mahon thought they should cancel her track season. "More than anything, she needed a break," he says. Deena made the best of it and traveled with her husband in Italy, biking through Chianti, tasting wine and enjoying good food in Rome and Florence. "We just vacationed, something we rarely get to do," Deena says.

On their way back, they stopped in New York so Deena could test-run the marathon route. She'd been deliberating over her fall marathon choice, a run at Chicago or New York. Both were high-profile races, part of the Big 5 in the World Marathon Majors prize series, and she had run both before. Race organizers for each city were vying for her, wanting to build the strongest matchups for their events. Chicago was a much faster course, a flat route that often produced records and where Deena had her first victory. But New York beckoned. It was the race that she had pledged she would win back in 2001 at her inaugural marathon. It was the race she had decided on.

7. Don't ever let go of your dreams

The 26.2-mile course through the five boroughs of New York crosses five bridges, adding too much elevation change for runners to break records. But it is the largest marathon in the United States, drawing more than thirty-five thousand racers and two million spectators. Each year, the winners get to ring the bell at the New York Stock Exchange and appear on the *Late Show with David Letterman*. New Yorkers know how to make something a big deal.

Deena had been struck by the energy of the event when she ran her first marathon here in 2001. It was just weeks after 9/11, and the city was still raw, wounded, and feeling the need to gather. "It was the most patriotic and inspiring event that I've ever been a part of," Deena told *The New York Times*. "Even before the race, I said, 'It's my dream to win this.'"

With one of the most generous prizes, the race attracts a roster of celebrity runners from around the world. Though Radcliffe, pregnant, was out for the season, a crew of impressive talent signed up. The previous year's winner, Latvian Jelena Prokopcuka, was in, as were Kenyans Ndereba and Chepkemei. Rita Jeptoo, the winner of the Boston Marathon, announced she would run as well. But Deena was the home-turf favorite. She got lots of calls for interviews; promoters used her image to advertise the race. "I like being the runner to beat," she told the media.

Race day had good, slightly cool weather, with sunshine and forty-degree temperatures marred only by a slight breeze. The elite women started off slow, in a clump. And they never got out of that cluster.

At mile 2, Latvian Prokopcuka broke away, chasing the pacesetter who'd gone out faster than the pack. A few miles later, Ukrainian Tatiana Hladyr gave chase. The duo led the rest of the way. The pack of world-class runners behind seemed to dismiss their breakaway. It was too early, Deena thought. Prokopcuka remained the forerunner for the rest of the race. For a short bit after the midway mark, Hladyr was a step ahead; but until near the finish, commentators mistook Hladyr for a pacesetter and ignored her presence. It was another strange element of a race that surprised many.

At mile 22, Deena realized she needed to act. She'd been waiting for Prokopcuka and Hladyr to fall back, but they hadn't. Now, Deena couldn't get enough speed. She'd been training on hills for a final push, but her strength just wasn't there. She finished sixth with a time of 2:27:54, almost a minute slower than her first New York run. Prokopcuka won, Hladyr was second, and Ndereba was third.

Deena was disappointed. She was the top American in the field, but it wasn't the race she had wanted to run. It was an odd run, Deena said afterward. "Tactically, it was a very strange race. I can only attribute it to the fact that there were so many accomplished women out there that nobody wanted to make a move."

She had trained so hard for this race and then, in the end, had been too careful. She'd said in advance she would run as conservatively and comfortably as possible in the race's first half, then push it in the second. But her strategy had backfired. "When you get sixth place, there are a lot of mistakes that add up," Deena said.

But she wasn't giving up, not by any means. "Winning this race continues to be my dream. I'll definitely come back to compete again."

Before the New York Marathon, seated in her kitchen on a sunny day in Southern California, Deena is certain she has her best races ahead of her. After we finish our snacks and iced tea, she repeats, firmly, that she hasn't yet run her fastest race. "I knew after London I could run faster than that," she says. "I'll keep running until that belief stops." Even after New York's disappointment, her confidence in the fast times ahead has not faded.

Taking the Stage

Wendy Hilliard

Rhythmic Gymnast Wendy Hilliard

Nine-time member of U.S. national rhythmic gymnastics team (1978–1988); first African American on national team (1978); U.S. national team coach (1988–1991); athlete coach for Olympics (1996); president and founder, Wendy Hilliard Foundation; cast member, Candide, *Broadway (1997); associate choreographer, AntiGravity dance and gymnastics company, New York; director of gymnastics and youth sports at Aviator Sports and Recreation, Brooklyn; president Women's Sports Foundation (1995–1997).*

Rhythmic gymnast Wendy Hilliard has what theater people call *presence.* In front of an audience, she lights up; she has a magnetism that captivates a crowd. "She loves to perform, she just sparkles," says longtime friend Christopher Harrison, a New York dancer and choreographer who was formerly a competitive gymnast. "Wendy has that thing on stage where she loves what she's doing so much it comes through every movement. She has this kind of charm."

But early in her career, she had to fight for her place on stage. As the only African American competitor at the highest level of rhythmic gymnastics in the early 1980s, she was told she didn't fit in with the other girls. Coaches tried to block her from the national team. But

Wendy would not be stopped; she fought back, both campaigning against race-based discrimination and proving beyond argument through a decade-long career that her skills were top tier. Today, she works to expand opportunities in the sport for everyone.

Rhythmic gymnastics is a less common cousin to artistic gymnastics, which features the familiar handsprings and flips on mats plus events on the uneven bars, the balance beam, and the vault. Mary Lou Retton, Dominique Dawes, and Kerri Strug made their names in artistic gymnastics. Rhythmic gymnasts, on the other hand, perform choreographed routines using balls, clubs, hoops, ribbons, and rope. The moves are elegant and flowing and demand incredible flexibility. Athletes kick into splits while twirling ribbons, contort themselves into human sculptures, and spin around as they toss hoops high into the air. Competitors perform individually or as a five-person team, dancing in 75- to 150-second exercises that are part ballet, part theater, and part acrobatics.

From the outset, Wendy, a natural performer, excelled in the sport. Her style reinterpreted the sometimes sedate, sometimes stiff traditions that had evolved through the sport's origins in Soviet bloc countries. On the mat, she shook things up. She was fast and athletic. She did triple jumps where others did doubles; she specialized in triple rolls when most others could only do two. For accompaniment, she chose pop music or soul, favoring Motown hits over the slow and lyrical pieces by Vivaldi that were often selected by the other girls. "I was from Detroit," she says. "It was my style."

And Wendy's goal in competition was not just to earn high scores; she liked to entertain the audience. "I was a performer. I was into giving a good show," she says. "I used facial expressions; I let them know I was enjoying myself."

No American rhythmic gymnasts have become household names. The sport has been neglected in the United States, suffering in part from attitudes that it is, as one commentator put it, "just a souped-up aerobics class." In the early 1990s, the International Olympic Committee briefly considered eliminating the sport from the Games. At the time, *The New York Times* sportswriter Jere Longman seemed to think this was a good idea, because, he wrote, "Let's face it, who can take a sport seriously when the inadvertent exposure of a bra strap means an automatic point deduction?" But athletes protest that those who criticize the sport for not being rigorous enough don't understand it. It requires just as much training, discipline, flexibility, and skill as any of the other gymnastics programs.

Wendy fell in love with gymnastics as a young girl growing up in Detroit. She watched the Olympics on television and dreamed of competing on the world stage someday. She was active and athletic, signing up for artistic gymnastics with an elementary school friend and also joining the swim team. Her mother eventually insisted that her youngest daughter choose between her two sports loves, swimming or gymnastics. Neither daughter nor mother—as chauffeur—had time for both. Gymnastics won. "I just enjoyed it more," says Wendy. "I was crazy about gymnastics."

From the start, Wendy pushed herself to excel. Her parents and her three older sisters inspired her. "My sisters and family in general are pretty driven, hardworking, and high achievers," she says. Her father ran one of the city's methadone clinics for the public health department. "It was an intense job," Wendy says. "He often got calls in the middle of the night." And her mother was a nurse and math teacher who became an administrator for the public schools. Both parents had graduate degrees. "In the black community at that time, that was a big thing," Wendy says.

Though she was the only athlete among the siblings, two of her older sisters were cheerleaders; she became a cheerleader, too. It was a good outlet for her gymnastics skills.

As a parent now, Wendy has a good perspective on the many ways her parents helped her to succeed. Her mother drove her to practices daily, usually taking two hours round trip. She would wait in the gym, doing paperwork or sleeping, as her daughter practiced for hours. Wendy's father woke her every morning for her running workouts with a glass of orange juice. And they funded trips to Europe for competitions, letting her take time off from school—despite the high priority they placed on education.

As she got better in the sport, Wendy advanced from the tumbling-focused city offerings at the Y to a better-equipped, more intense program in the suburbs. There weren't any programs with competitive teams near her home. Traveling out to the suburbs, she found herself in something of a different world. Wendy was the only black athlete on the teams. "This was Detroit in the late 1970s and 1980s, there was all this tension. I actually just became accustomed to being the only black," she says. "If you're doing what you really want to do, as I was, then the rest is secondary." Wendy says the rest of her world, at home, in school, and in church, was more racially balanced. "We lived in an integrated neighborhood and I attended integrated schools. I attribute this to keeping me grounded," she says.

This was a racially charged era in an economically fragile city. The big American automakers began automating assembly lines and outsourcing parts jobs in the 1950s, knocking Detroit's economy off its base. African Americans were hit especially hard. And "white flight" was changing the demographics of the city; in the 1950s, the white urban population declined by 23 percent. Racially motivated police harassment and brutality was shockingly common in black neighborhoods. The city's rising boil exploded in riots in July 1967. Over a five-day period, 43 people were killed, almost 1,200 were injured, and more than 7,000 people were arrested. The property damage to the city was estimated at $22 million. Wendy and her family did not live in the hard-hit, generally poor neighborhoods, but they were active in finding community solutions. Her father worked hard to quiet tensions and rebuild during and after the riots.

Perhaps because of news stories about the riots and other problems of the inner city, Wendy says some of her teammates seemed to have misplaced ideas about what her home life must be like. When she was dropped off by teammates one afternoon, some of the girls seemed shocked that her house looked much like their own. "They were clueless. They were like, oh, wow, this is where you live? We were in a middle-class neighborhood in northwest Detroit, the university district. I told them, 'We're just in the city; we're not in the hood.'"

The coaches who inspired her as she was starting out were the husband-and-wife team Vladimir and Zina Mironov. Zina had been a national rhythmic gymnastics champion in her home country of Ukraine before the duo was able to leave the Soviet republic; they settled in Michigan. As coaches, they took an exacting approach, emphasizing discipline and precision. "They brought the Soviet-style training," Wendy says. "Zina had competed at the highest level. She was really talented."

The Mironovs introduced Wendy to the little-known rhythmic branch of the sport when she was sixteen. She'd been curious about the ribbons and hoops she'd seen around the gym. This was just as rhythmic gymnastics was being introduced in the United States. An outgrowth of the artistic gymnastics program in the Soviet bloc countries, rhythmic gymnastics emerged in the 1940s and 1950s, and the first world championships were held in Budapest in 1963. Wendy was intrigued by the new style and liked exploring different skills. And the performance-based form suited her.

Wendy did well in regional competitions. As rhythmic gymnastics took hold in American circles, proponents began talking about a national team. The United States tested the waters at its first international competition in 1973. By 1978, Wendy was ready to join the national rhythmic gymnastics team. She was seventeen and became the first African American athlete to represent the United States in the sport. She competed at the world championships in 1979 and 1981. The Americans didn't get close to matching the scores of the Soviet bloc countries—the only non–Eastern European country to do well internationally at the time was North Korea. But for such a new program, the United States looked strong. And the team was improving. Wendy was one of the most promising among them.

In 1983 she went to the Olympic training center in Colorado Springs for the six-week training session before the national team selection. Wendy had just returned from a competition in Bulgaria, where she had placed in the top five. She was ranked fifth in the country. She felt she was at her strongest. In Colorado, about a dozen girls were competing for the six spots on the team. But the athletes pretty much knew who was in the top group and who was there to build her skills for next time. "You can tell," Wendy says. "They do all of the hard choreography with the best gymnasts."

At the end of the training session, all of the athletes and coaches and trainers gathered to hear the new team roster. "This is our national team," a coach announced. Wendy remembers, "They read off the list. And they didn't read my name. Everyone looked at me. There was this total hush in the room."

The national team head coach, Alla Svirsky, told Wendy she hadn't made the team because she didn't look right with the rest of the group—all of the other girls were white. She would stick out too much. "Wendy, what are we going to do with you?" Svirsky said. "You just don't fit in."

As in ice skating and other sports that combine artistry with athleticism, rating rhythmic gymnastic performances is subjective. An athlete's appearance makes a difference: Outfits and demeanor can influence a judge; bra straps, as Longman points out, count. Style is a large factor in the scoring. And in the group exercises, synchronicity is highly important. But no one, up until that time, had told Wendy that the color of her skin limited her opportunities as an athlete.

The team had been chosen by a committee that included judges, coaches, and program directors. Wendy's absence from the list was also surprising because she had been on the national team before. But, she later learned, one of the coaches who had been a key advocate for her on that first team was no longer there to fight for her.

After the announcement, Wendy was in tears. "It was hard," she says. "I thought, *What do you expect me to do?* Yeah, I stood out, there's no way around it. I knew in my heart that you can't tell me that and expect me to accept it. It wasn't like I didn't have the skills. At this point I'm at the elite level. I'm not going to sit out for a year. I'm not going to change colors."

With her parents' encouragement and support, Wendy wrote a letter to the president of USA Gymnastics, the sport's national governing body, protesting the decision. After reviewing the circumstances, a decision was announced: The team roster would be changed. Officials at USA Gymnastics overrode the earlier selection process and established the national team based solely on ranking, taking the country's six highest-rated athletes—which included

Wendy. Svirsky withdrew as national team head coach. Wendy and the rest of the athletes went to the world championships in France that year. They placed eighteenth out of twenty-one teams.

Wendy went on to compete with the national team for five more years. She was voted team captain twice. Teammates later nominated her as an athlete representative to speak for them with USA Gymnastics: "Let's vote for Wendy," one said. "She knows how to fight."

Looking back on the incident, Wendy is thoughtful. She went on to work with Svirsky for many years afterward on the national governing board for USA Gymnastics and says Svirsky was very sharp and talented as a coach. "I knew her well and trained in L.A. with her for many months. I think Alla did not realize that you could not keep me off the team because of my color," she says. "I think that the coaches that came from the former Soviet Union did not realize that you could not make decisions based on race and on a whim. It was an interesting dynamic; many of the coaches were here because they were Jewish and had had a very rough time in their respective countries. They knew discrimination. They didn't get that you couldn't do it here. I think this was a big lesson, a wake-up call, for Alla."

She thinks that, at the time, Svirsky and others were so focused on following the Soviet model that they believed American athletes should look Eastern European. "Most of our coaches were trying to get us to look more like them. They didn't realize you can't up and do it like that," Wendy says. "I don't believe in her heart she was against me because of my color. She wanted the power to pick her team."

It's hard to document, but Wendy's outspokenness may have made things more difficult for her in future competitions. As in artistic gymnastics, athletes are rated by a panel of judges on a point scale. After the 1983 decision, Wendy suspected she had some adversaries sitting at the scoring table. "It made it harder for me to get good scores. I would go to Europe and would win third place. In the United States I couldn't get a score to save my life," she says. "I was used to getting it in judging. It's hard to counter that. Some of them weren't so happy with me, they saw this little athlete going against the system. I was ruffling the feathers of some people." Yet Wendy would not be cowed; she refused to be anybody but herself.

The national-team drama unfolded a year before rhythmic gymnastics had its debut at the Los Angeles Olympics. For those Olympic trials, Wendy just missed the cut. She came close, but not close enough, to making the cut again for the 1988 Olympics in Seoul. She missed the eighth and final spot by a fraction of a point. "That was the most heartbreaking thing," she says. "My coach was crying. At that point I decided to stop."

Wendy was twenty-seven, and she was ready to move on. She retired and settled in New York. She had studied Russian and broadcasting at Wayne State University in Detroit and wanted to complete her degree—which she did that year, with honors, at New York University.

But she wasn't finished with gymnastics. She started coaching, forming a team with students at the United Nations International School in Manhattan, which serves UN families. And she started working with Aliane Baquerot, a ten-year-old at the elementary school. Aliane had studied ballet, and she had a promising gracefulness.

Wendy spotted Aliane's potential and took her under her wing. "Wendy was amazing," says Aliane. "She's a great combination of strict and caring. She knew me so well. She would correct me when I was doing something with my back turned, and I'd roll my eyes. I was a teenager. And then Wendy would say, 'Don't roll your eyes at me.' I couldn't get away with anything."

Wendy says she modeled her coaching style on the methods of her Ukrainian coaches. "Being a champion in sports is not rocket science," she says. "You do it six hours a day for ten years, you're going to be pretty good. Coaching is tough, though. I'm pretty hard-nosed. When I have my other coaches working, then I come in, it usually moves to a different intensity level. My motto is if you expect a lot of the kids they will give it to you."

Wendy coached Aliane for eight years, guiding her to the 1996 Olympics in Atlanta. Wendy had come so close to the Olympics as an athlete, and now she would attend as a coach. "Wendy told me to enjoy every moment. To focus on the competition and to enjoy it," says Aliane. She placed ninth in the group exercises, and retired after the competition. Today, she works as an actress in Los Angeles.

During this time, Wendy was also able to continue to perform—in a New York kind of way. Shortly after starting coaching, she worked with her friend Christopher Harrison, also a retired gymnast, on a post-race show for the New York Marathon. He was choreographing the production and wanted something full of energy that would grab the attention of the tired runners. He planned a dance number, but instead of pirouettes and jetés, he staged handsprings and cartwheels and tumbling. "Wendy was the first person I called," he says. "She has a really strong performance quality, a cross between a ballerina and Janet Jackson."

Wendy was so captivating, Harrison says, that he put her on stage alone at several points in the show so he could give the rest of the troupe time to rest between numbers. She was able to carry the whole stage herself. A Radio City Music Hall producer saw the show and asked them to perform in the Rockefeller Center theater. For this show, Wendy developed a two-ribbon breakdancing routine that became her signature, creating something no one had ever tried before in rhythmic gymnastics. "How often do you find a rhythmic gymnast who's funky?" Harrison says. "People loved it so much."

Harrison went on to found an innovative dance/acrobatics performance group called AntiGravity, with Wendy as associate choreographer. The troupe performs acrobatic aerial circus-dance shows all over the world, wearing antigravity boots and using techniques inspired by bungee jumpers.

At Harrison's insistence, around this time Wendy was able to realize a lifelong dream to perform on Broadway. Harrison pushed her to audition for a Harold Prince revival of the musical *Candide*. Wendy was busy coaching and didn't have much time to rehearse a number and learn lyrics for an audition song—especially when she wasn't confident of her singing voice. But Harrison knew she had Broadway-level stage presence. "You've got to audition," he told her. "I'll take care of the song. And I promise you won't have to learn lyrics."

Wendy showed up for the audition in front of famed producer Prince and handed the accompanist her sheet music. The pianist cracked up. But he went ahead and began to play.

Wendy may be the only performer in Broadway history to audition for a show to the tune of "Ta-ra-ra Boom-de-ay." She's definitely the only one to do that and get the part. But it's a testament to her finesse that Prince, laughing so hard he was holding his sides, was first to call her for a spot in the chorus for the show.

Since the time when Wendy was an athlete through the years she'd been a coach, the demographics of gymnastics had not changed much. At U.S. competitions, Wendy didn't see a lot of African

American athletes. (Dominique Dawes was heralded as the first African American gymnast to medal in the Olympics in 1996. On the 2006 national rhythmic team, there was only one African American athlete out of eight competitors.) And at that point in her career, Wendy was in a position to extend opportunities to a broader group of kids.

In 1994, she started the Wendy Hilliard Foundation to offer gymnastics classes to kids in Harlem. The nonprofit program quickly grew from a small class to serving more than three hundred kids—from the area and surrounding neighborhoods—per session, with workouts and dance classes in an improvised gym at a church and at a community athletic center. Classes are held weekly, sometimes more often, for kids as young as six to those in high school. After a decade, the program has reached more than five thousand kids.

Teaching kids who had no gymnastics experience at all was a big change from training elite-level athletes. "It was different, totally," says Wendy. "I got good at working with a lot of kids. They were city kids, all the sports they'd done were stuff like basketball. Gymnastics is very different, it's very disciplined. You have to stand in line, you have to speak softly, and you have to do things fifty times. The kids get individual attention; we have to know their names. They loved that kind of focus."

The program has had a big impact on many of the kids. They look up to Wendy. "It's awesome to be coached by Wendy," a fifteen-year-old student told *The New York Times*. "She's the person I want to be like."

Though she finds coaching overwhelming and exhausting at times, Wendy is very good at it. Harrison says she is good at breaking down the steps involved in a tricky maneuver. "She has the ability to articulate how she does what she does. She's able to take other rhythmic gymnasts and explain to them, get them to meet her at her level," he says.

The students had difficulties Wendy hadn't encountered with her elite teams. The focus was not on refining skills to perfection but on adapting to the capabilities of students on that particular day. "Everybody was on scholarship," Wendy says. "I wanted them to pay what they could, but nobody could pay. And they didn't have a lot of resources. Some were in shelters, or being raised by a grandparent. It could be hard because gymnastics takes time. And the kids had a lot of drama in their lives."

Several of Wendy's students have advanced to high levels, competing in the Junior Olympics and placing on the future stars national teams. This is really impressive, Harrison emphasizes: "Wendy contributes so much to the community. It's very, very difficult in Harlem to teach, just to get the kids there every day is hard. And to turn them into champions is amazing."

Every summer, the foundation stages a fundraising gala show by all of the young athletes. Wendy calls in friends from her competitive gymnastics days, from her connections on Broadway and in New York's performing arts scene. One year the legendary coach Bela Karolyi came, Wendy recalls. "It was great," she says. "The kids gathered around him. He says, 'Kids, I want you to work hard.' He gives them this speech. But it's loud in the gym, and he has this thick accent. They didn't understand a word he said. But they just said, 'Yay, Bela!'"

Wendy doesn't miss coaching at the highest competitive level. When she did so, she was only able to work with a small number of people. But her foundation has made it possible for her to broaden her scope. And she finds satisfaction in the small steps her athletes take. "The competition is not my driving force anymore," Wendy says. "What gets me most is giving kids opportunities to just do something. I'm just as excited watching them learn how to do a cartwheel. That's cool with me. That's just as much fun."

Today, Wendy splits her time between running her foundation, raising her two sons with her husband, Robert Mensah, and managing the gymnastics and youth sports programs at the new megacomplex Aviator Sports and Recreation in Brooklyn. The twenty-five-acre facility, a public-private project in Gateway National Recreation Area, opened last year in an effort to provide more recreation opportunities to city residents. Wendy is looking forward to bringing some of her foundation students to the well-equipped center to train, while still continuing to offer the classes in Harlem.

Because of her experience working with the Olympic committee as a coach and the fundraising skills she developed with her foundation, Wendy was appointed to the board for planning New York's bid for the 2012 Olympics. She worked for six years on developing the city's bid. Though the International Olympic Committee eventually chose London as the host city, Wendy said the experience was eye-opening. To establish the project's viability, she worked to identify venues and accommodations for the Olympics' wide range of sports, for all kinds of athletes from the Olympics and the Paralympic Games. In many ways, the city's facilities fell short. She says it expanded her view of equal opportunities.

"Looking at the Paralympic Games, I saw that the inequities were really tough. You wouldn't believe it," she says. "I had seen myself the racial thing. But this widened my vision. I saw the importance of fighting for rights for all sports."

There's a graceful line to the circle of Wendy's career: As an athlete she was nearly pushed out of her chosen sport by racism, and now she's working to reshuffle the deck to make it easier for the next generation. And she's continually widening her view toward inclusiveness. Wendy has long been a natural on stage, but her main focus now is playing to all members of the audience—and getting all of the audience members to play, too.

The Book of Karen

Karen Smyers

Triathlete
Karen Smyers

First place Timberman 70.3 2006 New Hampshire (4:34:36, half-Ironman distance); twelfth place Hawaii Ironman 2006 (9:39:59); ninth place Hawaii Ironman 2005 (9:30:47); fifth place Hawaii Ironman 2001 (9:48:34); winner USA Triathlon National Championship 2001 New York (1:55:57, Olympic distance); second place Hawaii Ironman 1999 (9:20:40); winner International Triathlon Union long-distance world championship 1996 Muncie (4:11:00, 1.9 km, 90 km, 21.6 km); third place Hawaii Ironman 1996 (9:19:13); winner Hawaii Ironman 1995 (9:16:46); first place International Triathalon Union world championships 1995 Cancún (2:04:58, Olympic distance); first place Pan American Games triathlon 1995 Mar del Plata, Argentina (2:04:52, Olympic distance); second place Hawaii Ironman 1994 (9:28:08); winner Pan American Games triathlon 1993 St. Croix (2:33:13; Olympic distance); winner world championships 1990 Orlando (2:03:33, Olympic distance).

Doctors say that a broken bone can grow back stronger after an injury. In healing, sometimes the newly knit-together bone becomes thicker than the original, creating an extra layer of protection against future impact. In the same way, world champion triathlete Karen

Smyers has returned to the sport over and over again, each time with greater determination, despite freak accidents, devastating injury, and incapacitating illness. She is living proof of the power of attitude in achievement.

Karen certainly got lucky at the starting line—she was born into a talented, supportive family with good looks, smarts, and a knack for winning in every sport she tried. A competitive swimmer as an undergraduate at Princeton, she started racing in triathlons shortly after graduating; Karen found herself first to the finish line in nearly every race. So, the thought crossed her mind, why not turn pro and make some money while she's out there swimming, biking, and running? Without really planning it, she became one of the planet's best female athletes, winning world championships and the triathlon's most famous race: the 140.6-mile swim-bike-run endurance fest called the Hawaii Ironman.

Her life seemed charmed. She was a gifted athlete who could chalk up world-class race times, it appeared, almost effortlessly. But then, midcareer, she faced accidents, delayed recovery, motherhood, and a mystery disease. And here is where her character met its test. She tackled each challenge, creating opportunity out of misfortune and using setbacks to steer a new path for herself. After each blow, she returned to race again. In fact, she hasn't simply waltzed through a charmed world, but has charmed and amazed the world with her resilience.

"One failure doesn't mean you quit," she says. "Eventually it comes to you if you keep trying."

Slender yet broad-shouldered from many laps in the pool, Karen has an engaging, asymmetrical smile and an easygoing, self-effacing manner. This is unusual in a sport that appeals to goal-oriented personalities; triathlon is known for being full of hyperorganized type As who can devote long hours to training. It's for competitors who want to perfect their abilities not just in one sport, but in three. "There are a lot of athletes who train way more than I do," says Karen. "I've never been real structured. I used to think, *If only I were more disciplined.* But at this age, I'm not going to change my stripes."

Do what you're capable of on the day of the race—that's her motto. A forgiving and reasonable approach, but hardly the battle cry of a cutthroat competitor. It is one that has gotten her to the finish line of nearly every race of her career. And she is known for not suffering too much along the way; she has often praised the delights of having a beer or two with teammates, even in the middle of training. "She is so ridiculously normal and down-to-earth," says Dede Griesbauer, winner of last year's U.K. Ironman, who trains with and is coached by Karen in Massachusetts. "With her successes, somebody of her ability, it's surprising—she's still so laid-back."

Griesbauer has gone to Kona with Karen to compete in the Hawaii Ironman the past three years and has been astonished at her training partner's mellow approach. "It's a kick to see her the day before the race. You have a lot to do, you're running around, you have to check your bike in. That morning, my bike is all put together, my nutrition is where it's supposed to be, I'm ready to roll. Around four o'clock in the afternoon, Karen will look at her watch and ask, 'What time do we have to check our bikes? I wonder if I have good tires?' She gets it all done, of course. She just has an incredible perspective. She doesn't worry. She filters out the stuff that doesn't matter."

Now in her forties, Karen has seen the sport evolve from fringe to mainstream. The first triathlon in the United States was held in San Diego in 1974; four years later, the debut Hawaii Ironman combined three established endurance competitions, the Waikiki Roughwater Swim, the Around-Oahu Bike Race, and the Honolulu

Marathon, with a three-mile shave off the bike race to connect it all. (The race was later moved to the Big Island, adding to the challenge a section across rough lava fields for runners.) A consecutive race of swimming, bicycling, and running, triathlons test an athlete's versatility as well as his or her endurance. A competitor has to do well in three sports requiring different skills and muscles; she also has to transition quickly from water to land, from bike to run—with shoes preattached to bike pedals, sports drinks prepped, and snacks bagged and ready at the transition station. Distances range from short, super-sprint triathlons consisting of a 0.25-mile swim, 6.2-mile bike ride, and a 1.6-mile run, to the granddaddy of the sport, the 2.4-mile swim, 112-mile bike, and 26.2-mile run of the Ironman, an event that takes at best eight hours and up to seventeen (not that everyone finishes within seventeen hours, but after that time the course shuts down). The sport was added to the Olympics in 2000, with a mid-distance event comprising a 1,500-meter (0.9-mile) swim, 40-kilometer (24.8-mile) bike ride, and a 10-kilometer (6.2-mile) run.

A good attitude has helped Karen endure in such a grueling sport over such a long time, says Donna Smyers, one of her older sisters and a top age-group triathlete herself who holds the Hawaii Ironman course record for forty-five- to forty-nine-year-olds. "I think she's lasted so long partly because she never did get so compulsive about the training," she says. "People might be surprised at the number of workouts that have gotten skipped. Not because she didn't want to do them, but because it got dark outside. She never would beat herself into oblivion about that."

But somewhere wrapped beneath her worry-free exterior lies a reserve of determination. Despite giant setbacks, Karen has resurfaced again and again to swim, bike, and run at an elite level, fueled by her unshakable resilience.

Karen grew up in a suburb of Hartford in central Connecticut, the middle kid of seven children in a community that takes pride in being the oldest settlement in the state. Around Wethersfield Cove, wood-frame houses date to the 1700s, with plaques marking meeting sites between George Washington and the Comte de Rochambeau. From the second she could walk, Karen was involved in sports. She swam, did gymnastics, and played tennis in high school. "Early on, when I was about nine or ten, I remember riding my bicycle to my gymnastics lesson," she says. "And I had my tennis racket and my baseball glove in the bike basket. And I remember thinking, *This— my bike, my racket, my glove—this is all I need to be happy.*"

She was naturally competitive, especially with her brother Greg, two years her senior. "They used to torture each other endlessly," says sister Donna. "It just seemed like anything could turn into a competition with them. Or they would fight. Karen was very scrappy. If they were wrestling over something, or if they were playing sports, she could always play with the boys."

Though she played many sports, she excelled at swimming. "When Karen was in the eight-and-under group on swim team," says Donna, "I remember, she would just blow away the field. Her first meet she was five strokes ahead of the next kid. I thought, *Wow, how'd she learn to swim like that?*" She was a cocaptain for her high school swimming, gymnastics, and tennis teams. She went on to swim for Princeton and was a walk-on for the track team (after taking some time to convince the coach she could handle the workouts). She majored in economics and after graduation landed a job at a computer consulting company in Boston. Not knowing anyone in the area, she joined a running club to meet people. Her roommate, a friend from college, was training for a triathlon and suggested Karen join her. Karen signed up—and ended up winning the race. So she signed up for another—and though this time she only placed fourth, she caught the triathlon fever. "It got me hooked," she says. "I liked that it used my background in swimming but also involved new things. And it was an outlet for my competitiveness."

This was in the early 1980s. Triathlon was in its nascent stage. The Hawaii Ironman had yet to offer prize money; only 1,500 people belonged to the recently formed association USA Triathlon in 1982. By the end of 1986, the number had grown to just under 6,000. (In 2005, the group had more than 50,000 members.) Karen hadn't even yet heard about the Hawaii Ironman; she just enjoyed traveling to events and meeting people.

And she was competing well. Karen realized that if she'd been racing as a professional, she would have been winning prize money. "In 1984, the last race of the year, I saw I would have finished second in the race, which would have won me $500 if I had raced in the pro category. So I thought, *Next time I'm checking the other box* [on the registration form]. Back then, it was that easy to turn professional," she says.

Karen had been juggling training and her work at the Boston computer company. But the company wasn't doing well, and after scaling back her hours for a summer, it folded that fall. It seemed like a blow, but it was really a boon. With more time to train, Karen improved dramatically, particularly in the biking segment, which had been her weakest event. "I made a leap forward on the bike," she says. "After the company I was working for closed up shop, I got consulting work on a freelance basis. Knowing I could swim and bike on my own terms, with enough time to train, I thought, *Maybe I will pursue this sport.* I hadn't been taking it seriously—sports aren't supposed to be your full-time job. I'd been thinking I ought to use my education."

Competing professionally was still something of a lark. "The first year, I'd talk to my mother on the phone and she'd ask, 'So, have you interviewed anywhere?' And I'd say, 'I'm not trying to get a job, remember?'" she says. Then Karen started winning big races, with prize money. The purses back then were at best a few thousand dollars, but the sport and the awards were on the rise. (In 2006, the total purse for the Hawaii Ironman was $580,000.) She picked up sponsors, who provided stipends, bonuses, training clothes, and gear. "After a while, instead of asking about jobs, my parents would ask, 'So, how much did you win at that race?'"

By 1995, after a decade in the sport, Karen was at the top of her game. In the Hawaii Ironman, she outran Paula Newby-Fraser, at that point a seven-time winner who'd earned the title "the Queen of Kona," in the last quarter mile of the race for the title and a dramatic finish at 9:16:46. Her marathon run was the second-fastest time in the history of the women's race, at 3:05:20. That same year, only five weeks after passing Newby-Fraser at Kona, Karen won the International Triathlon Union's world championships in Cancún at the shorter Olympic distance race, in what *Outside* magazine called "the equivalent of hitting forty home runs and stealing forty bases in a baseball season." This was the sport world's unlikely, incredible dream—a player able to combine outstanding power with outstanding speed. And Karen had it.

Commentators wondered if she could topple Newby-Fraser's crown. Karen, *Outside* announced, "is finally at the top of the triathlon heap." The same article quoted Ironman champion Mark Allen's assessment of Karen: "She's made to do triathlon. She's got the upper body of a swimmer and the lower body of a runner."

And at this point in the story of an endurance champion enter elements from the most famous endurance story of all time. In the Bible, Satan points out to God that Job's devotion comes easily because his life is so good. A real test would be if he had to struggle, Satan suggests. All right, then, God responds to his fallen angel: Show me what you can do.

Karen was changing the storm windows in her house early in 1997 when suddenly, "in the blink of an eye," the glass slipped out of one frame and sliced open her leg, severing her hamstring. She had been scheduled to get on a plane the next day for a triathlon in Monte Carlo. Instead, she went to the emergency room. It was the first major setback she'd experienced in the sport. "I'd felt charmed up until that time," she says. It was the beginning of a saga out of the Book of Job.

It took months for her injury to heal. Karen made the best of it: "It was the perfect time for a maternity leave," she says. She and her husband, Michael King, a fellow triathlete and, at the time, owner of a popular runners' bar in Boston called the Eliot Lounge, had a baby girl, Jenna, the next year. "I look back on it as a blessing," Karen says.

Karen was back training eight weeks after her forty-eight-hour labor. "I think I came back [from the hamstring injury] without side effects. I was 100 percent afterward," she says. But it wasn't long before disaster struck again. While on a training bike ride when Jenna was three months old, Karen was sideswiped by an eighteen-wheel tractor-trailer. She broke six ribs, had a lung contusion, and separated her right shoulder. "I had to think long and hard about coming back and its impact on Jenna," Karen says of her feelings after the accident. "I thought about how close I came to taking away her mom. And while I was recovering, I couldn't pick her up. I couldn't use my arm at all. I put her on pillows, I couldn't even nurse her without help. This accident was harder to recover from emotionally."

Ultimately, though, Karen renewed her commitment to competing. "I realized I do love the sport. And what it came down to is this: Accidents happen everywhere. I'd been riding for years. I thought, *Do I want to quit?* And the answer was no. I get too much enjoyment out of it. The good outweighed the bad."

The broken ribs were "painful as all hell," Karen says. But her physical therapist urged her to get back in the water swimming as soon as possible. She recalls her first time getting back into open-water swimming at Walden Pond, where, once in over her head, she felt like she might not be able to swim back to shore. Her therapist's push, she now realizes, helped her recover more quickly than expected. By 1999, she was having a good year, placing in the top seven spots in the triathlon World Cup, the Pan American Games, and the North American championships.

In the fall, she went to see a doctor because of swollen glands in her neck. She thought perhaps she had bronchitis.

An ultrasound showed that her thyroid was enlarged. Then the endocrinologist dropped a bomb. He said it looked fairly likely to be cancer. "*What?*" Karen said. "I was in complete disbelief. I thought, *I'm doing triathlons, so how could I have cancer?*"

Doctors advised her to have her thyroid removed. Yet Karen was set to compete in the Hawaii Ironman the next month. She'd been struggling to get back into competition for two years. Once the thyroid was out, she knew she'd have to go through another recovery. Who knew how long that would take? Her doctor agreed to postpone the surgery until after the Ironman competition. Karen made another request: Could they also wait until after the final race of the season, a shorter-distance triathlon in Mexico? Karen wanted to add this race to her roster in order to boost her rankings and put herself in a good position for the spring's trials for the debut Olympic triathlon in Sydney in 2000.

Karen placed second in Hawaii, behind Canadian Lori Bowden, with a time of 9:20:40. "I had the best race I could have had," Karen says. Bowden broke the run record to win with 9:13:02. Weeks later, Karen flew to Ixtapa, Mexico, on the Pacific Coast northwest of Acapulco. The competition was a "draft-legal" race, meaning a rider is allowed to ride closely behind another biker for the boost created by the lead biker's air vacuum. Karen pushed to come out of the water with the first group—starting out with the leading group of bikers in the middle leg would make all the difference in this race, she knew. But as they were biking, the woman in front of her had a fluke mechanical failure—one of her pedals detached from the crank—and crashed directly in front of Karen. "I fell over the top of her," Karen says—and broke her own collarbone.

Job wallows in self-pity for hundreds of years. Karen gave herself one international flight to break down. She had to head home immediately for her thyroid surgery. She'd hoped to get a seat in first class, to have extra space to nurse her collarbone. But there were no seats left. She found herself in coach. And in tears.

"That's when I hit rock bottom emotionally," she says. "I had finally gotten myself back into shape. The only thing holding me back was this broken collarbone. I remember getting pretty into self-pity, thinking, *This is not fair.*"

She was ready to tackle the illness the same aggressive way she tackled her races, but she didn't know what to do. "I understand what it means to tear muscles, but how do I fight this one?" she thought. "I had shrinking confidence in my body."

Two days later a biopsy confirmed she had papillary carcinoma. This is a minimally invasive form of thyroid cancer, so it was relatively good news. Karen had a thyroidectomy and several lymph node chains removed. Before she was sedated, she taped a handwritten note to her body that said: "Please do not move this shoulder." She didn't want her collarbone injury aggravated further.

It was a six-hour operation and revealed a lot of what doctors called "abnormal-appearing tissue" in her neck. They weren't sure they'd removed all of the cancer and planned to eliminate any remaining cancer cells with radioactive iodine treatment. Karen again asked if she could postpone the radioactive iodine post-surgery treatment until after the Olympic trials. Because it was a slow-growing cancer, the doctors agreed to the delay.

Meanwhile, her collarbone injury "ended up being a nightmare," Karen says. She was so careful, immobilizing it, that it didn't heal properly. The bone seized up, and she had virtually no mobility. "I was trying so hard to be the ideal patient, I practically froze my shoulder," she says.

The Olympic trials were held in two contests that spring of 2000, one in April and one in May. Her collarbone had just healed and she'd barely been able to get into the pool to train. But Karen competed, placing seventh. Only the top three candidates were invited to join the Olympic team.

It was a blow for an athlete whose talents were ideally suited to this mid-distance race. Karen was almost thirty-nine years old; the inaugural Olympics were her first and last chance to represent her country at the Games. Yet Karen was able to see the silver lining in this, too. "I look back on it as a fortunate thing," Karen says. "The trials were a really good motivator to get better. I put all of my energy into that and didn't do a lot of second-guessing or wallowing. I hardly remember much about the cancer. The trials made me push forward and focus on getting confidence back in my body."

That summer, she continued with her thyroid treatment, getting a test tracer dose of iodine to see how much thyroid tissue was left; she would later receive a large radioactive dose to null any remaining cancerous cells. In between, she went to a race in Cleveland and developed a hard lump on the side of her neck. She went to a hospital after winning the race and waited for hours to see a doctor. No one could identify the source of the lump. She saw three different experts. Finally, some medics came hurrying into the exam room. "Put this on," one said, handing her a mask. They pulled her to a back door. "We're going to escort you out here. We think you have the mumps."

She had to laugh. It turned out she didn't have the mumps. But her doctors at home finally figured out that her parotid gland had swelled hugely in reaction to the test dose—a reaction they'd never seen before, but who wouldn't agree that world-class athletes are a special group? Tests revealed that she still had cancerous cells, and she had a second thyroid surgery in August that year.

Karen focused on recovery. She'd wanted to return to compete in the Hawaii Ironman that fall after her disappointment of not making the Olympic team. "Always look forward," she says. But the surgery and recovery took too much out of her, and she realized she couldn't compete that year.

Still, she actually felt lucky. "It could've been worse," she says. "But I'm glad I knew enough not to say, 'I'm going to do Hawaii in 2000 no matter what.' By the beginning of the next year, I was feeling good. But I wouldn't have been able to race that year."

After nine months off, Karen came back strong. She didn't struggle with low energy or weight troubles the way some patients do on thyroid medication. She jumped back into competitions, winning the national championships and placing fifth in Hawaii. There was another thing she wanted from her body, though: a second baby. So she thought she'd hold off on competing in 2002. But she and husband Michael were playing a waiting game. "Every month, I was wondering, am I pregnant? By May, I decided, this is driving me crazy. It's like trying to watch a kettle boil. So I might as well start training," she says.

Michael was racing at Kona that year. A strong amateur triathlete, he'd supported his wife through six Ironman competitions and also had competed many times himself. Karen realized how grueling the training would be and figured, since she'd be going along with him anyway, she might as well slap a race number on, too.

Then, just when she was getting into a workout groove, "lo and behold, I got pregnant," she says. "I think what I needed was a distraction." Karen stopped training to minimize risks. She was, after all, forty and had had trouble enough conceiving. But then, days before she and Michael were to leave for Hawaii, she miscarried. She was saddened. Karen didn't know what to do, whether she should pack her race gear or not. She threw it all in, leaving her options open.

At workouts in Hawaii, she felt good. She told herself, "Okay, I'll just be happy I can do Ironman." The competition went well for the swim and the bike. But she started to have trouble during the run. She was over-heating and feeling extremely worn out.

She was only midway through the 26.2-mile run, and she felt worse than she ever had. "I didn't drink enough," she says. "I started to have pains in my lower abdomen."

Cramps due to dehydration are common for extreme endurance athletes. Bladder chafing is another common issue, also related to dehydration. It's an uncomfortable but not health-threatening condition. Karen thought this might be her problem. But, with her recent miscarriage, she worried maybe something more was wrong. "What if I'll never have another baby?" she asked herself. "I have a thing about dropping out of races," she says—before the Ixtapa accident, she had never dropped out of a race in fifteen years of competition. "But when your long-term health is at risk, that's a good reason to stop."

Karen asked for a medical consultation. She had to stop. Her competitors ran past. She was ushered to a medical tent and given an exam. Finally, after many questions, the doctors concluded that she was fine. "You're okay to continue," they told her. "Really?" she said.

She'd been ready to bail, take a DNF (for Did Not Finish) on her record. She'd lost her shot at the top spots and prize money. She'd been derailed for almost an hour. Back at the finish line, her parents were waiting with her daughter, Jenna; they were waiting to cheer for Karen, her sister Donna, and for her husband. *If I go back and wait with them, watching other people cross the line, how am I going to feel?* Karen wondered.

Do what you're capable of on the day of the race. This was the advice she'd given to countless athletes. This is what she'd said was her motto. This is what she would do today. It was time to walk the walk, she thought. She headed out, slowly, at a mincing pace—not even a run. At this rate, she'd finish a mile in fifteen minutes—more than double her usual time.

She was in the middle of the pack, jostling with the mass of competitors. "This is good experience for me," she thought. After getting some water at the next aid station, she started to feel better. She'd been able to cool down. And then she realized, "It doesn't even hurt anymore." She started to run.

"Good to see you again, Karen," fellow competitors called as she passed. The crowd cheered for her. She finished, with a time of

10:53:23; Donna was ahead of her at 10:43:39, winning her age group for the third time with a course record (she won in 2003 and 2005 as well). Michael finished at 11:49:24. Karen found herself sobbing at the finish line. The race had been a roller coaster. "It was the only time I cried at Ironman. I'm not a big crier. And I didn't want people to think I was crying because I did badly, it wasn't that. It was just emotional. I had held it all in until I finished and then the floodgates opened."

Karen finished in twenty-seventh place. After a second miscarriage, doctors adjusted her dosage, believing that one of her thyroid medications had possibly been causing her to miscarry. She gave birth to a son, Casey, in early 2004.

Karen continues to compete, training with her team in a leafy town outside Boston, not far from Walden Pond. She coaches fellow athletes and helped organize a kids' triathlon last spring that her daughter competed in. Now, at age forty-five, she shoots for top-five finishes, rather than first place. "I've had to adjust; I'm realistic," she says. "I'm probably over the peak." But she doesn't look entirely convinced. She, better than anybody, knows that her body holds plenty of surprises. She finished ninth at Kona in 2005 and twelfth in 2006. And in 2006 she won the half-Ironman distance Timberman 70.3 race in New Hampshire. "So occasionally I can go beyond top five still!" she says.

Teammate Dede Griesbauer says Karen never talks about the problems she's overcome to continue competing. But when Griesbauer had an early disappointment in one of her first major races, collapsing at mile seven and needing to be rushed to the hospital, Karen knew what to say.

"In the hospital I was shouting at my husband to call Karen. 'Just tell her I'm sorry,'" Griesbauer says. "I felt it reflected poorly on her. I insisted, so finally my husband held the phone up to my ear. And Karen said I was being ridiculous for apologizing. She was concerned for me. And she has this perspective; she'll say, 'Dede, things may not turn out the way you think they're going to. But life will go on the same no matter what. Win, lose, or draw, it goes on.'"

Karen takes her own advice: Do the best you can on the day of the race. "I've had disappointments along the way, sure. I would have loved to make the Olympic team. I would have loved the experience. But I've had a long career. I've been able to make a living at it, which is astounding to me. And to say I was the best in the world is phenomenal." She smiles as she says this. "I achieved more than I ever dreamed I would."

After Job's many trials, his wealth is restored to him at an even greater level than before all the trouble, and he builds a new family. In many ways Karen, too, is stronger for what she has faced. She has certainly achieved more than anyone thought possible, given the hurdles thrown in her path. "One thing that has been impressed upon me time and time again in my line of work is how absolutely marvelous the human body is," she said in a speech at Boston University in 2001. "Its ability to heal, especially if coaxed in the proper way, never ceases to amaze me. I have seen bodies—mine included—come back from what I thought was irreparable harm. Amazingly enough, not only do the bodies come back, but they sometimes come back stronger than they were before."

Perfect Matches

Misty May-Treanor

Beach Volleyball Player Misty May-Treanor

Ranked number one on Association of Volleyball Professionals (AVP) national tour (2003, 2005, 2006); ranked number one on Fédération Internationale de Volleyball (FIVB) international tour (2002); 503 career match wins with partner Kerri Walsh, second most of any women's team in beach volleyball history; 89 consecutive team wins, an international record (2003–04); 17 tournament wins in one year, a women's volleyball record (2005); gold medal Athens Olympics (2004); sixty-nine career first-place finishes; sixty-three career first-place team finishes with Kerri Walsh; FIVB best offensive player (2005); FIVB best setter (2005); FIVB most outstanding player (2005); AVP best offensive player (2004, 2005, 2006); AVP best defensive player (2006); AVP most valuable player (2005, 2006); AVP team of the year, with Kerri Walsh (2003–2006); Beach Volleyball America rookie of the year (2000); NCAA indoor volleyball champion, California State University, Long Beach (1998).

At the last beach volleyball match of the regular season on a sand court in Cincinnati, Olympic volleyball champ Misty May-Treanor appears calm as she waits for her opponent's serve. She and partner Kerri Walsh split the backcourt, bent forward with their hands on their knees—the best beach volleyball pair in the history of the sport. They wear matching black-and-white bikinis, adorned with a tropical flower pattern; Kerri is in her signature pink visor. Misty wears a black sweatband around her head, brown ponytail curled in a line at her back.

The match is tied. Misty and Kerri, atypically, lost the first game to Americans Jenny Johnson Jordan and Annett Davis, the second-ranked team for 2006. They had a sluggish start, but they rallied to win the second game. And they're ahead in this third game, a fifteen-point tiebreaker.

Kerri wears the logo of a sponsor, Gatorade, in a temporary tattoo on her bicep. A sponsor's name adorns Misty's sweatband, white blocks of words against the black material. Misty also has a permanent mark high on her back, above the left shoulder blade. It's a tattoo of an angel, wings outspread, and at its center are the initials of the person who has influenced her most in life—her mother, Barbara May.

Barbara was a competitive beach volleyball player in the 1970s who had a handful of wins early in the decade. Back then, the women's circuit was just getting started: The sport was invented in the 1920s in Santa Monica, but its popularity really exploded in the 1960s, when Americans were smitten with beach culture. At that time, Gidget movies were all the rage; surfing was catching on as a sport and as an appealing, alternative lifestyle devoted to sunshine and spontaneous living. It took a while, though, for the fun-in-the-sun game to be taken seriously, particularly on the women's side. During Barbara's competitive career, the women's games were sideshows to the men's. There was no professional league for women. It wasn't until 1986, after Barbara had retired, that the Women's Professional Volleyball Association was formed.

Barbara's contemporary Kathy Gregory, a top competitor in the 1960s and '70s who played for twenty-three seasons, says she sees a lot of the mother in the daughter's play. "Misty is old-school like her mom, and I think that's why she knows how to win. People don't realize what a tremendous competitor and fighter Barbara was," she told *DiG*, the volleyball magazine.

Misty says her mother gave her the drive to excel in the sport. Even after having her daughter in 1977, Barbara continued to compete on the local circuit. "I don't think I would have become the player I am today without my mom," Misty says. "I wouldn't be as successful. My parents didn't exactly push me, but we played a lot together. It was the three of us playing most of the time. They were of course very knowledgeable. When you have parents that are very competitive, you're going to pick that up."

Misty certainly had athletic genes in her favor. Barbara was also a nationally ranked tennis player. And Misty's father, Butch May, was also an outstanding volleyball player. He was on the 1968 Olympic indoor squad that surprised everyone with a win against the Soviet Union. (The team went on to finish seventh while the Soviets won gold.) Misty was practically destined to become a top competitor in the game.

It's impossible to talk about Misty May-Treanor's accomplishments without talking about her partner, Kerri Walsh. The duo has dominated the women's sport since they paired up six years ago, smashing opponents' efforts into the sand with killer spike after killer spike. They finished the 2006 AVP season in first place, winning thirteen of the fifteen tournaments on the national tour. The year before, they won ten of thirteen tournaments on the domestic tour, organized by the AVP. They won three out of eight tournaments on the international tour, run by volleyball's international organization, the Fédération Internationale de Volleyball (FIVB). The duo has set records in nearly every category, including consecutive wins, total domestic wins, domestic tournament wins, consecutive domestic tournament wins, set win percentage, match win percentage, and first U.S. Olympic gold. And they're still playing; Misty is twenty-nine; Kerri is twenty-eight. All remaining records are poised like a set ball hovering just above the net.

Misty and Kerri together have been ranked number one in the United States for the last four years. They have a record of 504 match wins to forty-five losses in ninety-three events, with sixty-three tournament titles. That's a winning percentage of 92 percent. They won every match they played from July 2003 to June 2004. That was eighty-nine consecutive wins over eleven months. Almost an entire year of victory. Shortly afterward, they started another winning streak, fifty consecutive wins over nine months. What other athletes out there can boast statistics that strong? How did this duo get so good?

"We've never seen a team like Misty and Kerri," veteran player Kathy Gregory told the AVP. Karch Kiraly, a legend in the men's game with twenty-eight years of play and Olympic gold medals in both indoor and beach volleyball, told *The New York Times:* "They are the best women's team I have ever seen."

One of the AVP circuit's longtime players, Elaine Youngs, agreed. "You find yourself out there thinking, *Can they make one mistake? Just one?*" she said.

In volleyball, in sports overall, there has never been anything like them.

Misty says the secret to their success is steadiness and hard work. While many of the other American women's teams have switched partners, reforming in new combinations sometimes in the middle of a season, Misty and Kerri have been unshakeable. "It's like many teams, the more experience you have together, the better you are," Misty says. "We've been through the thick and the thin."

They have a lot in common. Both grew up in California, not far from the beach; both played indoor volleyball from junior high through college. They even competed against each other as students, first in regional teams, then as undergraduates, with Misty at California State University, Long Beach, and Kerri at Stanford University. Misty is a year older; Kerri was so impressed with her that after a school tournament, she asked Misty for her autograph. Kerri, like Misty, has athletic parents and seemed preprogrammed for a life in sports. Her mother was a star indoor volleyball player at Santa Clara University in Northern California. Her father played baseball for the Oakland A's minor-league team.

The two make a well-balanced team. At six feet three inches, Kerri is more intimidating at the net, with incredible height and reach. Misty's modest (for volleyball) five-foot ten-inch frame looks almost short beside her teammate's. But she has, as several commentators like to put it, "coils for legs," jumping out of the sand to play formidable defense even at the net. Her play is impeccable, with nearly perfect timing and skills. She also has fantastic, instinctive court sense. She is one of those players who, uncannily, is always in the right place at the right time. Together, the duo does the best job of any pair of covering the eight-meter-square sand court.

In terms of personality, they also are a good match, a complementary one: Kerri is often described as reserved and quiet. Misty is a jokester with a goofy sense of humor. She hams it up for interviews;

after her introduction at the Cincinnati match, she ran out to the sand and did funky sprinkler-dance moves for the crowd.

From the day she started playing volleyball, Misty stood out. She joined junior high and high school squads near her hometown of Costa Mesa, about thirty-five miles south of Los Angeles in Orange County and not far from the sand at Newport Beach. "Everybody knew Misty was going to be a great beach volleyball player by age twelve," her trainer, Mike Rangel, told a *Cincinnati Enquirer* reporter in 2005. "We would see her do things and be like, 'Are you kidding me?' I think what makes Misty so great is she was raised around the game. Everything about volleyball is like second nature to her, like breathing and walking."

She was the best setter on the team at volleyball powerhouse California State University, Long Beach, playing the indoor game and bumping the squad to the 1998 NCAA championship. She became one of the most decorated players in the college game, named a three-time All American and the 1998 NCAA athlete of the year. She played for the U.S. national team and could have gone with them to the Olympics in 2000. But in 1999, shortly after her college graduation, she realized she wasn't enjoying the game as much anymore.

The regimented schedule of national team training and travel started to feel stifling. She had grown weary in a sport she'd been playing intensely for fifteen years. "If you had asked me back when I was in college, I would have thought I'd play indoor much longer. I would have been trying for beach maybe now," she says. "But I just got burned out. I don't think I had a summer off since junior high school. At the Olympic training center in Colorado Springs, it's like Groundhog Day every day. It's nonstop. I needed to get that fire back. With beach volleyball you have more freedom. You can set your own schedule."

Both volleyball and its beach cousin are American inventions. Indoor volleyball uses six-person squads that rotate positions on the court after scoring. The indoor sport was first developed in 1895 by William G. Morgan, a YMCA physical education director in Massachusetts; he wanted to create a game with less rough jostling than basketball but still offering an aerobic workout. The new game quickly spread to YMCAs around the country. Eventually, it was exported to other countries, and a competitive circuit was created. Indoor volleyball became an Olympic sport in 1964.

Beach volleyball is less controlled and predictable than the indoor game. Variables of sand depth, wind, and weather conditions create challenges. Instead of six players covering the court, there are only two. Though the beach court is slightly smaller than the indoor one, the beach game is more physical, requiring more dives and runs. And though it combines the athleticism of basketball and tennis with the challenge of an energy-sucking sand court, beach volleyball has never entirely shaken the misperception that it's really a frat-boy drinking game masquerading as an athletic event. It wasn't until 1996 that it was admitted to the Olympics.

The party atmosphere of beach volleyball, with rock music blasting and fans wearing swimsuits alongside the players, both adds to the appeal of the game and, perhaps, undermines the athletic achievements of the competitors. Some object to the women's bikini uniforms as unnecessarily revealing, though the player's handbook requires that athletes wear bathing suits.

Misty has heard the criticism many times before. "At first, people talk when they think we just show up at the beach and play. But when people know how hard I work, they change. Once they come down to the beach and see how hard it is just to walk in the sand, they stop. The bathing suits are comfortable. No one's criticizing track runners for wearing singlets."

But it's hard not to see that the sport sells the "babes on the beach" concept as much as anything else. More than athletes in any other women's sport, it seems that volleyball players turn up on Internet "sexy athlete" sites, where their athletic achievements are not the main draw. Misty ignores all of that attention. "I really feel sorry for the people who have nothing better to do than that," she says. "I don't really pay attention to it."

You can't play volleyball by yourself. Beach volleyball, particularly the most popular two-person-team version, is all about finding the right partner. (There's also a four-person game.) After a few preliminary practice competitions, Misty started her beach career with veteran Holly McPeak. Eight years older than Misty, McPeak today is one of the most experienced women's player on the circuit. Muscular and quick, she played her first competitive games in 1987, when Misty was ten years old.

They were a strong pair, improving from their first showing in 1999 with a ninth-place finish to consistent second- and first-place spots by early 2000. When they started out, McPeak was ranked twenty-eighth in the world; after six months, the two together were the second-ranked team. By that summer, they were pegged to win a first-ever U.S. beach volleyball medal at the Olympics in Sydney—but were disappointed when they were eliminated in the quarterfinals by a Brazilian team. They ended up in fifth place.

Their partnership survived only a few months beyond the Olympics. Misty realized she wasn't ready for the pairing's high-level pressure so soon after her start in the sport. McPeak was pushing to reach the top. But Misty still had a lot to learn about the sport, and she needed a partner she could grow with. "I wanted to learn the game and be able to make mistakes. It was one of those things," she says now, looking back on a matchup with a player she has faced numerous times since. "I had learned the game at such a fast pace. I wanted to take a step back."

McPeak found new partners, most notably Elaine Youngs. She remains the winningest women's volleyball player ever, with seventy-two tournament victories. On her tail, though, is Misty, with sixty-nine, and she'll likely break that record in 2007.

Throughout her career, Misty has had the vision to anticipate what will be best for her development. As a junior in high school, she was torn between playing soccer and volleyball. She loved both sports. "But it came down to the question, where do I see myself going further," she says. She chose volleyball. After college, she decided to switch from indoor to beach volleyball, finding a sport in which her skills could stand out. She jumped into it just before its popularity would surge. (She was instrumental in this growth, of course.) And she showed similar prescience in making a break from McPeak to find a new teammate.

Around the same time that McPeak and Misty parted ways, Kerri was looking to switch from indoor to beach volleyball. She had gone to the Olympics with the indoor squad, which surprised everyone with its better-than-expected fourth-place finish. But the grueling international travel of the U.S. national team indoor squad was not appealing. Neither did she want to play overseas. So she'd started thinking about switching to sand.

It was their parents who first connected Misty and Kerri. Because their kids had played in the same volleyball circles, the parents had crossed paths many times. They all knew each other. They discovered each daughter was looking for a partner. And they all thought Misty and Kerri would be a great match.

"Basically, our parents are brilliant," Kerri told a Florida journalist.

The sand court changes a player's timing; it's an even more dramatic shift than when a tennis player switches from grass to clay, or to court. Kerri said she was worried about her skills transferring over to the new sport, that she might be slow adapting and disappoint her new partner, considered the top American player. Yet Misty has said many times that Kerri was a natural from the get-go. After some top-ten finishes, the team placed first in a Portuguese tournament in 2001, six months after they'd joined forces. In 2002, they had five first-place finishes and three second-place spots out of eleven tournaments. And in July 2003, they began their record run through eighty-nine consecutive wins, which included fifteen tournament titles.

They had eleven months of victory after victory after victory.

Misty and Kerri have won more matches than any other team in beach volleyball history, with sixty-three titles on domestic and international tours. They lead the next-best team by thirty. They are so far above their competition, it's as if they're playing a different game.

After she returned from the Sydney Olympics, Misty bumped into baseball player Matt Treanor at a sports physical therapy center. They had an instant connection. Their first date was to watch a volleyball game with Misty's dad, Butch. "We got along right away," Misty says. They married in 2004, after Misty won her first Olympic gold and Matt finished his first season playing catcher with the Florida Marlins.

It's difficult having two professional athletes in the family, Misty admits. "It's good because we understand each other, we work out together, we do outdoor activities. But I wouldn't recommend it for a lot of people," she says. "You need a very trusting relationship. We never really see each other. We understand that right now these are our careers."

She says that in season, often the best they can do is keep up with each other's activities by following games on television.

Misty and Kerri's winning run ended in June 2004. They lost on June 6 to Jenny Johnson Jordan and Annett Davis in a close match, 19–21, 19–21. Misty was hampered by a pulled abdominal muscle and, after playing (and winning) in a subsequent tournament, she withdrew. She and Kerri had to forfeit several matches. "People said I should have played," Misty says. "But I knew what was right for me." She sat out the rest of the summer's tournaments; she wanted to be healthy for the upcoming Olympics.

Both Misty and Kerri had been frustrated by close-but-no-medal finishes at the 2000 Olympics. Misty's disappointment was the fifth-place spot with then-partner McPeak. Kerri had been on the indoor national team; they hadn't been favored to medal, but after unexpected victories over Croatia and South Korea, American fans and the players got their hopes up. But the squad lost to Russia and then to long-dominant Brazil, ending up in fourth place.

After giving Kerri a scary couple of weeks wondering if she'd have to find a new partner for the biggest tournament of her career, Misty was able to play in the Olympic Games. And in Athens, she and Kerri played like goddesses. They didn't lose a single match in the tournament, despite facing the world's best. In the semifinals, they beat Misty's former partner McPeak and Elaine Youngs. In the final, they bested the longtime top-ranked Brazilian team of Shelda Bede and Adriana Behar. The score was 21–17, 21–11.

The win marked a turning point for the pair and for the sport.

Misty and Kerri realized a dream they'd shared for years. They were ecstatic. Sports commentators chided that their only flub of the tournament was "whiffing" on their victory hug; instead of embracing, they clumsily knocked each other to the sand.

After the win, their attitude toward competing changed. "I play for fun more now," Misty says. "I feel like I set out to do everything I wanted to. Now it's all icing on the cake. I like the game still. But if, let's say, something were to happen now, if volleyball were taken away, I'd think, 'Okay, I did it and I'm fine doing something else.'"

Their victory launched the sport into the limelight. Prior to Misty and Kerri, beach volleyball had been a late-night, cable-channel television event. But their record-breaking winning streak got noticed, even outside volleyball circles. By the time the Olympics arrived, NBC was ready to air the match in prime time. And the stadium in Athens was filled to capacity with ten thousand spectators.

Marketers saw the raucous audience having fun in the sun, and opportunity flashed across their minds. Sponsors eyed the tanned, sculpted, victorious pair. Soon Misty and Kerri were appearing in commercials, magazines, and newspapers. They became household names.

"It changed a lot," Misty says. "People were coming to our house all the time, they had to close our street. I had a lot of appearances, and people recognize you once you've been on TV. It was good for the women's game."

Though Kerri and Misty have closed the roof on other Americans' aspirations for the last four years, their success has been very good for the sport in general. America, as everyone knows, likes winners; four aces couldn't beat these two. With the media attention and the gold-medal victory, they propelled beach volleyball from an obscure sport into prime time. And their finesse challenges other players to push themselves.

Even Holly McPeak, Misty's former partner, agrees. She told *Volleyball Magazine*, "Misty and Kerri have both elevated our sport in level of play, level of awareness, and level of domination. I know where the sport has been and where it is going, and it is great that they are strong role models."

The women's circuit continues to grow; AVP added two events last year and two events the year prior. Participation is up to record highs, both at the high school and college levels. Misty is surprisingly modest about their success. "I just want to improve something every year," she says. "Improve my jump serve or set with my hands more. My goal is to keep becoming better."

After the final match at the Olympics, Misty followed through on a plan she had had for two years. She opened up a prescription medicine bottle that her father had brought with him on his trip from California, and scattered some of her mother's ashes into the sand.

Barbara died of lung cancer in 2002, just as Misty was rising from her position as an outstanding player to her new one in the stratospheric realm. Barbara had been an inspiration to her daughter and her biggest supporter in the sport. Misty was so upset by her mother's death, she even considered dropping out of the game—immediately afterward, playing just brought up too many painful memories.

In 2000, Barbara had been undergoing chemotherapy but still traveled to watch her daughter play in her inaugural Olympic Games. Then, Misty had been disappointed that she hadn't been able to show her mother a medal finish; in Athens, she felt satisfaction at being able to bring her mother's ashes to the site of her gold-medal victory.

Misty says her attitude has changed a lot since her mother's death. "It's no longer about winning. It's not as important. I don't get upset if I don't win, because I'm still healthy, I can still walk off the court. It kind of put everything in perspective," she says. "I don't feel, *I have to win this.* All the winning in the world is not going to do anything to change things."

Despite the new attitude, the duo's dominance in the sport didn't falter after the Olympics. And it still hasn't.

Kerri and Misty launched another winning streak with the Olympic victory, triumphing in fifty matches from August 2004 through July 2005. They won a record number of tournaments—thirteen—on the AVP national tour in 2006. And though they won only three tournaments internationally, they played in fewer competitions. Their style seems to have evolved—it is more creative, less driven.

Currently, they're focused on preparing for the Olympic Games in Beijing in 2008. Misty says they never count out any contenders. The three-year-old Brazilian team of Juliana Felisberta Silva and Larissa Franca will provide some of their fiercest competition; they beat Misty and Kerri in an FIVB final in Italy last year and went on to seven tournament wins for the season. "Brazil and China right now are two powerhouses," Misty says. "All of the European countries are getting very good as well. You've got to look out for everybody."

Misty says her goal is another Olympic gold. But her attitude is philosophical. "Sure, it would be wonderful to have two gold medals," she says. "But what's the second one going to bring that the first one hasn't? It's icing on the cake. I just like the game."

Back at the Cincinnati game, the duo looks unflappable as opponent Annett Davis serves to Misty, the shorter teammate. This is a common strategy to avoid sets to Kerri for the kill. But always being the receiver forces Misty to do a large share of the work in the bump-set-spike rhythm of the game. She digs, bumps to Kerri, and leaps to the net for a spike and a point.

Davis and Jenny Johnson Jordan have clearly tired from their earlier sharp play. Winning one game against Misty and Kerri is a big accomplishment, something few teams on the tour manage to do. But it's all they can do; Misty and Kerri pull ahead. Their consistent, error-free play powers them steadily forward. It's not just their finesse, but also their endurance that has gotten them to the pinnacle of their sport.

Misty serves the final point. The score is 14–12. On the return, she dives for a dig, Kerri sets, and Misty leaps for the smash-down kill. And here Misty does what she does so well, what other players can't replicate. As she leaps, Davis at backcourt sprints to the left side, anticipating the shot. And Misty, midair, with eyes on the ball and on both her opponents simultaneously, makes a split-second adjustment. Instead of smashing left, she drops the ball to the right corner, a cut shot that drops exactly where her opponent isn't. Misty places it so it's impossible for either player to reach. For the twelfth time this season, Kerri and Misty win the tournament. They will end the AVP tour with more wins than any other women's team ever. Once again, they smash previous records—and their opponents' hopes—into the sand.

Swimming into the Future

Lynne Cox

Distance Swimmer Lynne Cox

First person to swim 1.06 miles in Antarctic Ocean (25:00, 2002); first to swim from Little Diomede Island to Big Diomede Island in Bering Strait, U.S./Soviet border (2:06, 1987); first to swim eight miles around the Cape of Good Hope, South Africa (3:03, 1977); first to swim Strait of Magellan in Chile (1:02, 1976); first woman to swim between North Island and South Island in Cook Strait, New Zealand (12:02:30, 1975); two Catalina Channel crossings (8:48, 1974 world record; 12:36, 1971); two English Channel crossings (9:36, 1973 world record; 9:57, 1972 world record).

When she was fifteen, in the summer of 1972, Lynne Cox made her first attempt at swimming across the English Channel. At the time, only 229 people had accomplished the chilly, twenty-one-mile-plus crossing. She walked into the water at midnight from Shakespeare Beach, at the south edge of Dover. She was full of adrenaline and ready to test how fast she could go. Lynne had spent a year preparing for this night, swimming daily in the ocean near her home in Southern California. She had researched everything about the channel swim, envisioning the rocky beach and the white cliffs of Dover, talking to swimmers who'd attempted the feat;

hundreds of times, she'd imagined immersing herself in the cold water. She had dreamed of swimming the channel—La Manche in French—since she was a little girl. On the boat escorting her across were her mother, an observer from the channel swimming association, and the boat's captain and his son.

The water was silky and very, very dark. After about four hours of swimming, in the calm of the early morning, she hit something with her arm. Something else rolled off her leg. There were suddenly lots of round objects in the water, knocking into her. "What's in the water?" she called to the captain. Turns out, in one of the funniest sports moments ever, she was swimming through an overturned shipload of lettuce heads.

Near dawn, Lynne could see the outline of the French coast, a dark shape on the horizon. She struggled to pull herself through the tidal current just off Cape Gris Nez on the French coast. The final mile of the swim was the most challenging. She kept pushing; she'd come so far. The tide was powerful; it was moving her off-course in a direction that would add five difficult miles to her route. She pushed herself harder than she ever had before. And when she hit the rocky shore, she announced to French spectators words she had been practicing for a year: "*J'ai nagée La Manche.*"

She set a new world record, for men and women, with a time of nine hours and fifty-seven minutes.

Lynne Cox has floated herself in swimsuit and goggles on journeys no one else has ever attempted. She was the first woman to swim from the North Island to the South Island in New Zealand, the first person to swim across the Strait of Magellan, the first person to swim across the international border in the Bering Strait, the first to swim eight miles around the Cape of Good Hope in South Africa, and the first person to brave a mile swim in the frigid seas of Antarctica.

"She is the most economical swimmer I have ever seen," says noted neurologist and author Oliver Sacks. He and Lynne became friends through their shared love of open-water swimming—both had published essays about it—and they meet for ocean swims whenever possible. "She hardly uses her legs and could get along, I suspect, breathing on every tenth stroke. But she's very powerful, too—I saw this especially when she was battling stormy seas off Long Island one day."

Tall, with long, straight brown hair and a line of thick bangs that highlight the curve of her prominent cheekbones, Lynne is, in a way, also an ambassador from another land. In her many days spent paddling in the ocean, she has observed the graceful motions of swimming bat rays, heard the distinctive musical chattering of dolphins in the water, and seen the sun shimmering off four-foot-wide giant ocean sunfish called Mola mola warming themselves at the ocean's surface. Lynne describes a world so exotic, it's as if she's an astronaut come back to report on another planet. She has explored worlds no one else has, in a way no one else could handle.

Lynne's achievements have earned her a lot of publicity. Her two books, *Swimming to Antarctica: Tales of a Long-Distance Swimmer* and *Grayson,* have both been bestsellers. She now gets recognized on the street and in restaurants. She finds the attention unnerving.

A woman in a San Francisco hotel asked her to help her interpret her dream from the night before: "I was swimming with whales in the ocean and they were throwing oranges in the air. What do you think that means?" the woman asked.

"That they're California whales?" Lynne suggested.

But she's also been flattered by the attention. Teenage boys have asked for her autograph. She received more than seventy-five requests in 2006 from aspiring open-water swimmers looking for advice. It's time-consuming to assist every hopeful athlete, but she tries to give each request what she can. "I had people who helped me," she explains. Still, she says she's always relieved to get back home to her routine of swimming in the ocean. And planning her next open-water swim. It's in the works, but she's not ready to reveal where it is.

Lynne discovered her talent for open-water swimming when she was fourteen, a year before her English Channel swim. At that time her observant swim team coach, Don Gambril, who would go on to work with many world-class swimmers, including Mark Spitz, pointed out that she was stronger at the end of pool workouts than at the beginning. Lynne had been on the swim team for years, but had not excelled in the group (though, to be fair, she was on a highly competitive team that included two future Olympians). Gambril noted that it was a matter of finding her distance. He thought Lynne would do well on much longer swims, distances greater than any current Olympic events. He recommended she try open-water swimming.

Shortly afterward, she signed up for a local race, the Seal Beach Rough Water Swim. And from that first competition in open water, Lynne loved it. She started early that morning in a three-mile distance competition. "I swam as if I had learned to fly. I raced across the water," she writes in her memoir, *Swimming to Antarctica*. "My strokes felt powerful, and I felt strong, alive, as if awakened for the first time. Nothing in the swimming pool gave me this pleasure."

She was the first woman to finish and placed third overall among all swimmers, male and female. She was so giddy from her success, she swam two more races that same day, winning the two-mile second event, and placing behind one other woman in the third contest, a one-mile race. Lynne explains her enthusiasm for this newly discovered sport with a shrug: "I was so bad at so many things: I broke my foot in gym, and broke my elbow playing basketball in the seventh grade. When you're good at something, that sure feels better than being bad."

Lynne was part of an athletic, creative family. Her older brother, David, excelled at swimming from an early age; her two younger sisters, Laura and Ruth, became outstanding waterpolo players for the U.S. national team. Their parents encouraged them to excel in sports, particularly swimming. Their mother was an avid swimmer who had grown up around the lakes of her native Maine; she taught each of her children to swim, in the bathtub. Their father, a doctor, was devoted to healthful living and exercise. When Lynne was twelve, the family moved from New Hampshire to Southern California, to Los Alamitos, at the south end of Los Angeles County, a few miles from where the San Gabriel River empties into the Pacific Ocean. Her parents thought the Golden State would offer their four children better sports opportunities.

After her success in that first open-water race, Lynne immediately joined a squad of teenagers who were training to become the youngest group to swim the San Pedro Channel, between Santa Catalina Island and Seal Beach on the mainland south of Los Angeles. Lynne and four others ages twelve to fourteen left from the island in the middle of the night. They wore bathing suits, goggles, and caps (following traditional English Channel rules that disallow wetsuits). Assisting them in the crossing were several lifeguards and parents on kayaks, a paddleboard, and in a rowboat; their coach and more parents were a half mile ahead in a motorboat. The boat was dimly lit; they didn't want a lot of light because that would attract fish, and the fish would attract sharks.

"You don't realize how dark it really is until you swim through that water," Lynne says of that experience; it was her first distance swim in open water. The route is just over twenty miles directly across, but of course swimmers, battling currents, end up traveling a greater distance. Only 133 people have swum across the channel since the first swimmer, George Young, made the crossing in 1927.

The group of teens swam a bit erratically at first. They started out fast in a V formation, then slowed; they bumped arms in the darkness and startled each other. After the first hour, they settled into a rhythm, swimming hard and steady at the pace they had trained for. "We had never swum in such blackness. We couldn't see our own arms or our hands pulling right beneath our bodies," Lynne writes in *Swimming to Antarctica*. "I felt as if I were swimming through a black-and-white photograph of the sea at night. Without color, the world I swam through was in stark contrast, reduced to luminous blacks, brilliant whites, and tonal grays. Looking up toward the sky on a breath, I watched the brightest stars travel across the heavens as we moved across the sea. Each time I breathed, I looked deeper into space, seeing stars beyond stars."

They arrived on the sand at Palos Verdes in the early afternoon the next day, the first teenage team to complete the distance, with a time of twelve hours and thirty-six minutes. This was just the first of many challenging distance swims Lynne would undertake. And her swims would grow more and more difficult, in increasingly harsh environments, taking her to Chile, Argentina, Russia, Peru, Sweden, Finland, Alaska, and Antarctica.

Lynne's determination was astonishingly mature for her young age. "It is amazing to think of the combination of her absolute firmness of purpose and tenacity and dedication with such a sweet, easygoing nature," says her friend Oliver Sacks. Lynne says her parents modeled this for her, and her brother and teammates were her inspiration. "From an early age, my dad showed me how to set goals, how to work toward something," she says. "I had teammates who were Olympic gold medalists. I had a big brother I really looked up to, who was really goal oriented. When you have that kind of influence around you, you think big."

Her parents were entirely supportive of her dreams. They drove her to workouts that started as early as four or five o'clock in the morning. Sometimes they walked the beach as she battled the waves offshore, helping her practice steady pacing. And her mother traveled with her twice to England for her English Channel swims. "I said, I want to swim across the English Channel, will you help me. And they said okay," she says. "My parents thought it was normal."

Though her parents encouraged Lynne's dedication to swimming, she didn't feel she entirely fit in with the other teenagers at her high school. She had lots of friends, particularly from her swim group and on the waterpolo team. But with training taking four hours a day or more, she didn't have much free time for the usual high school parties and events. "I was not caught up in the dating scene," she says. "I wasn't involved in, 'Can I go out with him?' 'Will I be invited to this dance?' I sort of wanted to do all that stuff, too. In many people's eyes I was unapproachable. I didn't want to be unapproachable. Though I was different—I had a different focus at that time."

Unlike athletes who follow more established paths, Lynne has largely had to invent her route as an open-water adventurer. There is no medal event in the Olympics that comes close to the distances Lynne excels at, and no open-water-swim nationals tournament. Crossing the English Channel was the ultimate achievement of open-water sport, its Mount Everest. She felt at age fifteen that she had accomplished her highest goal. And she was left with a question: What next?

One immediate target appeared weeks after her first English Channel swim, when a fellow American from Massachusetts broke her just-established record by thirteen minutes. At first Lynne wasn't ready to plan another attempt, but by the following summer, at age sixteen, she returned to England and established a new, faster world record with a time of nine hours and thirty-six minutes.

But Lynne knew she wouldn't be back for another English Channel attempt. The idea of traveling the world and attempting things untried by others appealed to her more than shaving the record more and more. She had been taught to dream big, and so she set her sights on greater adventures and new experiences. And she was beginning to seek challenges that fused worldly affairs with athletic achievement. She saw how she could make a statement in the water. Back at home, there was one statement she wanted to make: She still had something to prove in attempting to cross the San Pedro Channel again.

During the first Catalina crossing, Lynne had had a hard time staying with the other teenagers in her group. Her natural pace was so fast, she kept getting ahead of her teammates; slowing down actually made the swim more difficult because she got cold. But they had all pledged to swim as a team, so she treaded water and did whatever she needed to in order to remain with the group.

Then, near the end of the twelve-and-a-half-hour swim, the two boys in the group sprinted to the beach. Lynne chose to stay with the remaining girl, who had slowed by this final stretch. (The third girl on the team had started to get hypothermic midway across and had had to abandon the swim.) When a *Los Angeles Times* reporter interviewed the group on the beach that morning, one of the boys boasted that they had beat the girls on the team.

"I just bit my tongue," Lynne says. "But that bugged me. I could have gone way ahead. But the idea was to swim together all the way.

As a team we made it across. But I went back to swim for the record." She wanted to try crossing the channel without being held back, to see how fast she could go. On her first attempt, fog rolled in so thick she had to give up because she couldn't see her boat. On her second attempt, she set a new world record, besting by two minutes the record her brother had established two years before and also beating the best time of her boastful young teammate.

Open-water swimming is one of the rare sports in which women often have a physical advantage. Size does not matter as much in this sport as it does in many others. And the greatest challenge for athletes is avoiding hypothermia by maintaining an adequate body temperature. (Also important, of course, are stamina, strength, and mental tenacity.) Women, with higher body-fat ratios, tend to have an easier time keeping warm and are generally more buoyant.

This is why the best open-water swimmers are not feather-weights. Lynne is solidly built. On her first English Channel swim, the taxi driver who was taking her and her mother to the starting point at the beach looked at her in the rearview mirror and said to Lynne, "You don't look like a channel swimmer to me. You're too fat to be one."

Lynne was stung. But her anger from that comment fueled her to swim faster that day. "It made me furious that somebody would say that," she says. "I was thinking, *How do you know what I can do? He's wrong,* I told myself. And I used that anger during the swim, I used it to motivate myself."

One morning while she was training for her second attempt at swimming from the Catalina Islands, Lynne noticed strange things happening in the water. First thousands of baby anchovies swarmed around her, plunking out of the water and sounding like a rainstorm. Then thousands of grunion swarmed around her; they were chasing the anchovies; the grunion were followed by tuna. Then she felt the water "hollow out" below her, like "a spaceship moving right below," she writes in her book *Grayson* about the experience.

She didn't know what it was, but when she started to head in to shore, a friend on the pier stopped her: He'd noticed a baby whale following her. He was afraid that if Lynne swam in, the baby whale would beach itself and die when the weight of its body collapsed its lungs. The baby, only a few months old, had gotten separated from its mother on their migration to Alaska and for some reason had adopted Lynne as its guide. So Lynne spent the morning swimming offshore with the baby, looking for its mother.

"Which raises a good question," she says. "How do you find a mother whale in the ocean?"

She didn't know exactly what to do. But she knew it was important for her to make the effort to help. "There are moments in life when you know that something is put in front of you, you have a choice. You can choose to do something about it, but you have to stretch yourself beyond what you've done before," she says. This was, she realized, one of those big moments.

The experience led to an epiphany. In her uncertainty in the ocean that day, after swimming for hours offshore, getting cold and hungry and feeling helpless in her effort to help a creature she didn't understand, she wondered, *How long should I wait out here?* And the answer: She could wait as long as she needed to.

"The waiting is as important as the doing: it's the time you spend training and the rest in between," she writes. "It's the space between the notes, the intervals between fast and slow, that makes the music."

Lynne calls on this wise, steady approach to guide her swims. "I learned how to hold on to something through swimming," she says.

A year later, when Lynne was a junior in high school, a trip to New Zealand opened her eyes to the wide-ranging potential of her swimming efforts. She was attempting to swim between New Zealand's North Island and South Island in the South Pacific, crossing the treacherous Cook Strait. Only three men had ever successfully swum across the twelve-mile strait, and no woman had ever accomplished it. The surging currents, swirling around the tip of each island, were very difficult to push through. On that day, storms that Lynne and her crew believed would be too far south to affect conditions were in fact churning up five-feet- to eight-feet-high waves. The winds whipped from fifteen knots up to forty. After five hours of struggling, Lynne learned she'd actually been pushed backward, farther away from her landing spot than where she'd started. She wanted to give up.

But she had many fans urging her on. Her team was in the boat by her; a reporter was watching. Most New Zealanders had crossed the Cook Strait by boat; they knew how tricky the currents were. A local radio station was following Lynne's attempt, and when she began to struggle, the station canceled its regular programs to continue a live broadcast of her fight.

Supporters began calling the boat—dozens of them. A ferry came by with hundreds on board cheering for her. "I was having such a hard time," says Lynne. "But people from all over New Zealand were calling. The prime minister called. I just felt like, okay, I'll keep going." Then pods of dolphins appeared in the water, chattering;

their energy buoyed Lynne. After twelve hours, she finished the swim. And she realized, because of the enormous support and media attention, that a swim could rise above athletic achievement to something larger. Swimming could give her a powerful voice.

Lynne saw that through her actions, she could speak to people. She thought she would dream really big: She would bridge borders and swim between the United States and the Soviet Union.

This was Lynne's senior year in high school; it was 1976. The cold war was still raging; Mikhail Gorbachev had yet to announce his glasnost campaign. Lynne envisioned a swim between two small islands in the Bering Strait connecting Alaska and the Soviet Union. Lynne wanted to cross the international date line as a symbol of peacemaking and cooperation. She wanted, she said, to swim into the future.

Starting that year, Lynne spent eleven years campaigning to make her dream happen. It was an enormous undertaking. No one had ever thought to do something like it before. The Soviet island where Lynne wanted to land, Big Diomede, was a military outpost and cloaked in secrecy. Though it seemed impossible, Lynne dug into the project, writing letters to President Ronald Reagan, Secretary of State George Shultz, the American ambassador to the Soviet Union, the governor of Alaska, two senators, and Soviet president Mikhail Gorbachev. She visited the Soviet consulate in San Francisco and was followed by the FBI and Soviet intelligence agents.

It was a physical as well as political challenge. The distance was only 2.7 miles, but the water temperature was forty-two degrees and dropped near Big Diomede to thirty-eight degrees. The landscape was battered with storms, fog, and tricky currents year-round. Lynne worked with doctors at the University of California, Santa Barbara, where she'd enrolled in college, who tested her reaction to immersion in cold temperatures. They discovered she had an unusual ability to maintain her core temperature despite being exposed to extreme cold. Her body was better able than others to control blood flow to her extremities.

It was an enormous project to organize a crew in Alaska, raise money, plan logistics for travel, and campaign for permission from embassies, the Coast Guard, the Soviet Sports Committee, and local American officials. After a decade, Lynne decided to move forward even though she had not gotten permission from the Soviets and did not know how all the details of lodging and equipment and support crews would work out. In 1987, she went to Alaska with a group of supporters and found people willing to help her along her journey. Finally, the day before the swim was scheduled, Lynne and her crew in Wales, Alaska, got word that Gorbachev had given permission for the Americans to enter Soviet waters and land on the island. She had asked the Soviets to provide a sleeping bag, so she could warm herself after the frigid swim, and a *babushka*, which she thought meant a colorful Russian shawl. For the photos that would be seen around the world, she wanted to put on something to symbolize the linking of cultures and goodwill that her swim would symbolize. She was told they would comply with her requests.

Lynne was thrilled and relieved when she finally received permission. She headed out on a foggy morning with several support boats holding a crew of doctors and journalists, escorted by Little Diomede residents in walrus-skin boats. Most of the residents of the American island had lived their lives less than three miles from Big Diomede but had never crossed into its waters, let alone set foot on Soviet land.

The water was so cold it stung Lynne's skin. She had trouble breathing. She didn't know if she would be able to make the crossing, despite the years of effort and all the support she'd received. It was difficult to navigate, impossible to see, and the boat captains appeared to be lost. It was the greatest physical challenge she had attempted. No one had ever done what she was doing. But she didn't want to let her team down; she couldn't abandon her eleven-year project and all that it represented.

When a Russian boat appeared out of the fog, Lynne could not believe her elation. She swam to the island, her arms gray with cold and tears of happiness in her goggles. She and her crew were greeted by a carefully selected group of Soviet luminaries and press representatives. The Soviets had spent a million dollars to welcome her with pomp and style: They provided warm welcome stations, blankets, a buffet feast, hot tea, and a warm tent for Lynne to recuperate in. After a cold press conference, Lynne hurried into the tent, and here a woman doctor set her up on a cot with a sleeping bag and provided hot packs to restore her body temperature. As Lynne lay on the bed, the woman spoke to her in Russian and showed her a few photographs of young boys and girls. Lynne asked if they were her children, and the woman shook her head. "I *babushka*," the woman said.

Lynne thought, *You're a colorful shawl?*

She hadn't known that the word *babushka* in Russian really meant *grandmother*. She had asked the Soviets to provide a grandmother, and they had.

The impact of Lynne's swim was confirmed months later during a monumental international event. Gorbachev traveled to the White House to sign the INF Treaty with President Reagan. It was the first international agreement to reduce nuclear arms and signaled a historic turning point for efforts toward world peace. In toasting the moment, Gorbachev said, "Last summer it took one brave American by the name of Lynne Cox just two hours to swim from one of our countries to the other. We saw on television how sincere and friendly the meeting was between our people and the Americans when she stepped onto the Soviet shore. She proved by her courage how close to each other our peoples live."

Lynne's swim had not only broken barriers of what had been thought to be physically possible, but she had helped, by doing the crawl in some very cold water, to break down the great political barriers of her generation.

After the Bering Strait swim, Lynne traveled all over the world. She had new challenges in mind; peace activists and environmental groups and political leaders invited her to come swim in their countries. She crossed Lake Baikal in Siberia, the Beagle Channel between Argentina and Peru, and Lake Titicaca at an elevation of 12,500 feet on the border between Peru and Bolivia; she swam from East Berlin to West Berlin; she crossed the Gulf of Aqaba from Egypt to Israel. Meanwhile, she graduated from college and worked as a swim coach and a librarian. And she was constantly searching for the next big challenge.

She found it in the Southern Hemisphere.

Lynne wanted to swim with penguins, diving into the waters of Antarctica. No one had ever attempted this. Most people thought a person couldn't survive for more than a minute or so in such cold water. "I wanted to stretch farther out than I'd ever stretched before," Lynne says of her motivation. "It's about exploring how far we can go, what are our limits. I wanted to go way beyond and try something really, really difficult."

She spent three years preparing for this challenge, with aerobic conditioning, weight training, and many cold-water sprints in the ocean and in an unheated swimming pool. In December 2002, at age forty-five, with a medical crew traveling alongside her, she left from a cruise ship and swam 1.06 miles across Neko Harbor to the Antarctic continent. The water was thirty-two degrees; it was like swimming in a bowl of ice cubes—sharp-edged, enormous ice cubes. The cold water was thick, like Italian gelato, and it pricked at her like broken glass. She had difficulty at first; her mind felt as stiff as her cold limbs. The coldness made it hard to breathe; her whole body felt like it was in a vise. But by the end of the swim she was able to relax; she admired the undersides of glaciers. Chinstrap penguins slid off the ice and swam with her in the water: "They zoomed under me in bursts of speed, and their bubbles exploded like white fireworks," she writes.

Lynne has seen a world few humans will ever experience. She's been unafraid to jump into places frightening to others. "When you're an open-water swimmer you have a lot of time out there to think. You spend hours meditating about what your hopes and goals are," she says. "And you're at one with the water. You can feel the ocean's energy. There's a lot of spirituality in open-water swimming."

Her accomplishments are also due to her ability to see the world in an entirely fresh way; she's been able to envision a path linking places others saw as unbridgeable. She's tried to join many worlds, connecting countries and helping sea animals and describing overlooked or forgotten or just unimaginable places. Lynne's greatest achievement is her ability to see the possibilities in the rough waves surrounding us all.

Speaking from the Court

Tamika Catchings

Basketball Player Tamika Catchings

Starting forward for Indiana Fever since 2002; WNBA defensive player of the year (2005, 2006); WNBA All Star (2002–2006); team leader in points (2002–2005); WNBA league leader in steals (2002, 2005, 2006); gold medal Athens Olympics (2004); WNBA rookie of the year (2002); ESPY college player of the year (2000); national championship University of Tennessee Lady Volunteers (1998); All American all four years of high school and college.

Only a few seconds remain on the overtime clock in the tenth game of the season for the professional women's basketball team the Indiana Fever. The score is tied 78–78 and forward Tamika Catchings has the ball just above the free throw line. She dribbles, crouches, her weight is on her toes; she fakes to the right. For a split second, she looks straight at New York Liberty forward Ashley Battle, as if to say, "Ready?" Then she moves—she glides to the right, stutter-steps, and dribbles through her legs to change direction. Her defender is forced back as Tamika carves out the space she wants on the floor. She charges once more, then abruptly pulls up to shoot from fifteen feet. The ball rolls halfway around the rim and drops in as the overtime buzzer sounds. Tamika has won the game for her team.

The crowd roars. Teammates swarm around Tamika for hugs and high fives. It's just another night for the star forward; in this game, she racks in a season high of thirty points.

Tamika Catchings knows how to dominate the court. At six feet one inch and 167 pounds, with square shoulders and sculpted arms, she is everywhere at once, moving with a quick, powerful grace. With her hair raked back in a headband and her lips curled over her teeth in concentration, she is so confident on the floor, so commanding, that plays simply have to go her way: Jostling down the court with opposing player Battle, she gets the layup and the foul. Midcourt, opposing forward Cathrine Kraayeveld keeps running two steps before realizing that Tamika, league leader in steals, has snatched the ball from her hands.

Tamika has been a force in the WNBA since her debut in 2002, after a record-setting collegiate tour at the University of Tennessee. She has a winning combination of strength and speed, offensive and defensive skills. Legendary player Houston Comets forward Sheryl Swoopes says Tamika is the most difficult player in the league to guard. "I have so much respect for her as a player and person," Swoopes told *Sports Illustrated*. "She won't slack off . . . she brings it for forty minutes."

The women's professional basketball league, the WNBA, opened up unprecedented team-play opportunities for female American athletes. Now with thirteen teams and thirty-four games during the summer season, the WNBA has surprised more than a few naysayers by its continued existence. Of course, it wouldn't be around without the financial support of the men's league. The average audience size is about 8,500, and most teams are not profitable on their own. But the WNBA celebrates its tenth anniversary this June, while dreams for women's professional soccer, a national women's softball league, and a professional gymnastics circuit have all fizzled.

The league's relative stability has allowed the game to grow. In 2003, Mark Adams wrote in *The New York Times* that the WNBA offers possibly "the best live-action value in professional sports." Critics complain that the women's game lacks the excitement of the men's flashy above-the-rim play; traditionalists applaud the women's emphasis on the basics, such as set plays, passing, and teamwork. The women players certainly rely more heavily than the men on team effort. In the NBA, showy slam dunks and in-your-face rebounds have made many players stars, but the style of play tends to emphasize the individual, not the team. "Our game is more about fundamentals," says Tamika. "That's the way that basketball started. Some people say if you don't dunk it's not exciting, but I think our game is."

Money makes a big difference, too; the average NBA player's salary is $4.5 million; the average WNBA player's is $47,000. The men make a *hundred* times more. And when you're talking about millions of dollars (don't forget the endorsement deals, as well), you're talking about an entirely different world for players, both on and off the court. It's easy to see how a difference in income changes your lifestyle and your options. Also, it can clearly change your play. The men in the NBA are making more money than they could anywhere else; most of the women players are choosing to earn less money than they could elsewhere so that they can do something they love.

And Tamika loves the game as much as anybody. "I just love everything about it," she told a reporter for *Indianapolis Woman* magazine in 2002. "I love being on the court. I love the ball. I love the way it sounds when it bounces. I like the fact that you can get better, and you can see your improvements as you get better."

The twenty-seven-year-old African American, who grew up mostly in Chicago, represents a new generation of women athletes.

She plays aggressively and skillfully; she is fluid and fast; she is powerful and throws her weight around when necessary; she owns the court. And she always has. Seattle Storm All Star Sue Bird isn't the only one who sees the WNBA's future in Tamika. "As time goes on, I think she is going to become the best in the league," Bird told a WNBA promoter. "She never stops moving offensively, defensively, diving on loose balls, all over the place."

Ever since she played on two state championship teams in high school, Tamika had her sights set on professional play, eyeing the WNBA since its inception during her junior year in high school. Unlike generations of women before her, since she became eligible, Tamika has always had the option to choose a path in professional sports in the United States.

You could say Tamika Catchings was born with a basketball in her hand. Her father, Harvey Catchings, played in the NBA for eleven seasons; he played for the Philadelphia 76ers, the New Jersey Nets, and the Milwaukee Bucks. The family followed the six-foot nine-inch defensive specialist to Italy for a pro season, where the Catchings kids hung out with Joe Bryant's son, Kobe. Tamika spent a lot of time at the gym. "I always loved to go to my dad's practices," she says.

Her father coached her and her sister on a basketball team when she was in the third grade. Harvey ran weekly drills with his eldest son, Kenyon, his elder daughter, Tauja, and his youngest, Tamika, in the driveway of their home in a Chicago suburb. He says he let them get by him maybe once every third try. This was when Tamika was six. It's easy to imagine Tamika, twenty years prior to her game-winning fakes against the Liberty, practicing the same moves with her father. Today, no one *lets* Tamika do anything on the court—she claims what she wants, creates the plays she needs to score.

All of the Catchings kids were gifted athletes. Kenyon was an All American in high school, but a stomach disease sidelined him after graduation. Tauja went along with the family sport, though she didn't love basketball the way her younger sister did. Despite her early distaste, however, she went on to become a star player for the University of Illinois basketball team and played professionally in Sweden and in the WNBA for the Phoenix Mercury.

As girls, Tamika and Tauja liked very different things: Tamika wanted only to be dribbling on a court somewhere, while Tauja cajoled her younger sister to join her in play with Barbies and Cabbage Patch dolls. "I loved my dolls and clothes and all of the 'girlie' things that Tamika couldn't stand," says Tauja. They alternated activities in negotiated sibling cooperation: "We would play twenty minutes with the dolls for twenty minutes of basketball," says Tamika, who hated playing with the dolls. "It was the worst torture ever. She'd get mad at me. Some of the dolls' heads would come off. The hair would be cut off."

For Tamika, it was always all about basketball. She didn't want to do anything else in her free time. Her father called her a basketball addict. When Tamika couldn't talk her sister or anyone else in her family into playing, she'd go outside and walk through moves, or sit in a corner and visualize a game on her own. "I'd play by myself, I'd play even if I didn't have a basketball. Your imagination can take you far," she says.

One reason Tamika liked basketball so much is that on the court she found a place where she didn't feel vulnerable or different. She was born with a hearing problem in both ears, the cause of which was unknown; though she isn't entirely deaf, many words sound fuzzy and indistinct to her. She couldn't even hear her own voice very well, so her speech didn't sound like everyone else's. Tamika wore clunky hearing aids behind each ear, and glasses as well. A lot of her classmates teased her. "I looked different, I talked different," she says. "I had what some people called a disability."

She hated wearing the hearing aids, and one day in third grade she ditched them, refusing to wear new ones. She relied on lip reading and tried to disguise her hearing problem from others. "When people made fun of me, I'd say, 'All right, let's take it to the court,'" she says. "The kids that played sports, most of them were outgoing and pretty or handsome. I didn't fit in. Playing sports was the only time I could be better than everybody."

In basketball, she could, silently and convincingly, be the best.

Tamika is extremely close to Tauja, who's older by a year. Tauja is her de facto manager and her best friend. They live ten minutes from each other in Indianapolis and see each other every day when Tamika is in town. Sometimes they still play basketball together: "I'll typically rebound for her and play dummy defense if she needs me to," says Tauja.

They were inseparable when they were younger. During those years, Tauja was her sister's voice. "Wherever Tauja was, I was. She spoke for both of us," Tamika says. "I was with Taj 24/7. I didn't have my own friends. We'd do an interview, and I'd be like, where's Tauja? They'd ask the questions, and she'd answer them for me."

The duo played basketball together at Stevenson High School in Lincolnshire, Illinois, and led their team to a state championship in 1995. But during that same time, their parents divorced. Their mother, Wanda, wanted to move back to Texas to be closer to her family. Kenyon was already in college, and Tauja was entering her senior year and didn't want to move. So Tamika volunteered to move with her mother to Duncanville, Texas, outside Dallas. "I just came home one day and said, 'You know what, Mom, if you want to go, I'll go,'" Tamika says.

They scouted out a place to live that summer while Tamika was in Texas for a basketball tournament. Once they moved, though, Tamika started to have second thoughts. She had never been on her own before. She was in a new place, about to go to a new school. And she'd always had her sister there to speak for her. The night before her first day at her new school, Tamika was filled with regret. "I cried and cried that night. I talked to my sister on the phone and I talked to my dad. I was kind of mean to my mom, telling her, 'I can't believe I came down here.'"

But as soon as they saw how she could play, for both the volleyball and the basketball teams, the students at Duncanville High School were delighted with the talented Chicago export. "All the girls on the teams, they just grabbed my hand and said, 'Come on with us.' That first day was great. I came home, I was excited, I had new friends. It was a great chance to grow up. I had to speak for myself."

As a preteen, Tamika had pledged that she would play professionally when she got older. She'd planned to try out for the NBA, but in her junior year, after the women's team won gold in the 1996 Olympics, a women's professional basketball league formed. "The WNBA is even better," she thought.

She chose University of Tennessee for her college career, after a lot of research and after considering attending University of Illinois so she could play with her sister. About two hundred colleges recruited her, and Tamika wrote notes back to every one of them. But

Tennessee was her first choice from the outset. The school has been the dominant force in women's college basketball for two decades (with regular challenges from archrival University of Connecticut). And this is due to its intense, hard-driving coach, Pat Summitt.

Summitt is the winningest coach in Division I basketball history. She is a legend in the sport, famous for placing high demands on her players. She is vocal and fiery. She has smashed the rings on her hand while banging her arms against the wood floor in frustration watching a game. Right away, she told Tamika that she needed to relearn how to play defense. Tamika, of course, had been a star everywhere she'd played up until that point, and she was not used to such blunt, sweeping correction. Maybe she hadn't made the right choice, she worried. Summitt was concerned about her new player's tendency to take her criticism so hard. "When I would say anything to her in practice, it would break her heart," Summitt told *The New York Times*'s Mark Adams.

But Tamika eventually found her way and improved her game. Her freshman team included stars Chamique Holdsclaw and Kellie Jolly Harper; they went undefeated in season and won the national championship at the Final Four. Tamika set a freshman record for most points at 711 and the highest scoring average at 18.2 points per game. She finished her college days ranked third of all time at scoring, rebounds, blocks, and steals, averaging 5.1 points per game over her four years.

She and Summitt developed a "great relationship," she says. "She's a true friend. She took care of us for four years. She taught us so much, not just about basketball, but also prepared us for life after basketball. Now when I see her, she says, 'I'm so proud of you.' You know, like proud moms will do." And recently, when asked by a Tennessee hopeful for advice, Tamika said, "Take the message, not the tone, with Pat."

In that first year, Summitt also pushed Tamika to do one more thing: She told her to wear her hearing aids. Tamika hadn't been able to hear the coach's instructions, particularly during games in the loud arena full of amplified, echoing noise. Tamika would ask teammates to tell her what Summitt had said as they jogged back onto court after time-outs. When Summitt caught on, she told Tamika that if she wanted to be a success in basketball and in school, she needed to wear her hearing aids.

Tamika did. And Summitt was right; everyone around her said Tamika blossomed once she could hear better. She was more comfortable speaking up. She understood more. The aids didn't really affect her play (and because they slip around, she doesn't wear them in games now), but off the court, "it made a huge difference," her father told *The New York Times.*

Tamika was leading her team in scoring and rebounding in January of her senior year when, as she came down from a jump in a game against Mississippi State, her knee buckled. She dropped to the floor with a snapped anterior cruciate ligament (ACL) on her right knee.

It was the injury that all basketball players fear, a season-ending one; for some, a torn ACL can end their careers. Two months after the injury, sportswriter Jere Longman published an article in *The New York Times* pointing to the epidemic of ACL injuries in women's basketball. Women are up to eight times more likely than men to tear the ligament in jumping and twisting sports such as basketball, soccer, and volleyball. By his estimates, ninety-five collegiate women basketball players tore an ACL that year. Doctors theorize that women athletes may be at greater risk than men for ACL injuries because of their wider hips, but, Longman reported, "there is no clear understanding of the causes."

Tamika's college career was cut short; she was out for the second half of the season. Largely because of her absence, her team didn't make the Final Four. Tamika had to look forward to the WNBA, hoping she could shine again there. Before the injury, most had expected her to be number one in the draft picks; with a vote of confidence in her recovery, the Indiana Fever picked her third in the first round. Tamika tried to rush her recovery to play for the 2001 season, but a reinjury setback forced her to sit out the entire season.

She made up for it the following year, her first in the pro leagues. Tamika averaged 18.6 points per game, was first in the league in steals and averaged 8.6 rebounds per game. She was a leader on the team, which included veteran guard Bridget Pettis and new draft pick Kelly Schumacher. Tamika was named rookie of the year and led her team to its first playoffs. *The New York Times* called her "the most exciting player that the rapidly advancing women's game has yet produced." Hall of Fame guard Nancy Lieberman told the paper, "Catchings is the now and the future of the game. I've played and coached against the best players in the world, and no one has played like she does."

In September that year, she traveled to China with the national team for the world championship tournament, starting alongside superstars Lisa Leslie and Sheryl Swoopes. In the final, she scored sixteen points and nabbed eleven rebounds, pushing the team to a close gold medal victory at 79–74. And in 2004 she traveled again with the best players in the game to the Olympics in Athens. She had dreamed of playing in the Olympics since watching the team four years earlier while training on the Junior Olympics squad. The team went undefeated in the tournament, and Tamika averaged 6.9 points per game. They won gold.

"I was ecstatic—just having the opportunity to play with Lisa [Leslie], Dawn [Staley], and Sheryl [Swoopes] was incredible," she says. "And winning the gold medal, standing there after on the platform, the flag goes up, and the national anthem plays—man, not many people get the chance to play for their country for the medal. It was a feeling, like, golly, we've done it."

It was a golden summer and validating for the league that formed out of the rising tide of enthusiasm for women's sports after the 1996 Olympics.

Through basketball, Tamika found her confidence and her voice. And as she settled into her professional career, she realized it was time to give back. She had always done volunteer work, starting with her family's efforts when she was a young child. "In the NBA, the players started off having to do a lot of community events. My mom and dad made sure the three of us were there to help out," Tamika says of her childhood. She says it gave her and her siblings a sense of the importance of doing good in the community. "We were seeing toys that we wanted, that we had to give away to other kids. From a very young age, we were instilled with a sense of the importance of being able to give. That when you're fortunate, you give back. That kind of grew as I got older."

She began volunteering in Indianapolis shortly after her move there to play with the Fever, donating her time to sports camps. Right in the center of the state, Indianapolis has a population of just under 800,000 people and a poverty rate for families of 11.5 percent. A recent educational study ranked the state twenty-third in the nation in high school graduation rates. In 2005, a local paper's report on sweeping reorganizations in the public schools called their current state "abysmal."

Tamika is working to improve opportunities for kids in Indianapolis. In 2004, she started the Catch the Stars Foundation, devoted to offering literacy and sports programs to at-risk children in the city. She established a reading center at a school in town, founded a biannual eight-week girls' mentoring program, created a college scholarship award program, and every year hosts a holiday basketball camp and a four-day Thanksgiving food drive fitness clinic that collects more than a thousand pounds of food for charity. The three-year-old foundation is run by a staff of thirty-five volunteers.

In the off-season last winter, Tamika played for a Moscow basketball team; her Thanksgiving fundraiser events ran during the same time as their season. So, in order to cover the two-weekend fundraising commitment, she played in Moscow Monday through Thursday, then flew home in time to lead the weekend workshops, before flying back to Russia Sunday night.

She has also been vocal in national issues, speaking out to protect Title IX when the legislation was threatened with an overhaul in 2003. And she was one of three WNBA players to travel to Louisiana after Hurricane Katrina as a goodwill gesture with a players' union group.

"More than anything, I just want to make a difference," she says. "I want all kids to have opportunities."

Tamika says that her hearing difficulty never slowed her down when she was playing. "Basketball is a game of sign language, in a way," she says. And she says her actions have always spoken her sentiments most clearly.

"My greatest strength as a player is in my ability to be a leader," she says. "I'm not the most vocal, but I lead by example. I love to be a great teammate. I try to make sure that we all know we win together and we lose together."

After Tamika's overtime shot to win against New York, the Fever went on to win twenty-three games for the season. Tamika led her team to the playoffs for the second time. She was honored before the game with the league's defensive player of the year award (for the second year in a row) and then went on to score seventeen points, six rebounds, and five assists in the first game of the semifinal series. But her effort that night wasn't enough to win, and their opponent, the Detroit Shock, triumphed 68–56.

In the third quarter of the next game for the best-of-two series, Tamika took a nasty fall backward from under the net, smacking her head hard on the floor and getting a mild concussion. She sat out for ten minutes, and her team missed her. By the time she returned in the fourth quarter, the Fever had a ten-point deficit. Tamika couldn't bring them back.

The loss ended the season. Tamika led the league in steals and ranked for the season in the top ten for points per game, rebounds, assists, and blocks. Her efforts earned her top votes for the All Star game. But she was still disappointed. However, even after sitting out with her head injury, once back on the court she never let up. She never does.

"I put everything into it," she says about her play. "I play 110 percent effort. That's what I do." Her sister agrees. She stands out as a player because of "her heart," Tauja says. "She never quits and is absolutely relentless. Plus, she loves the game. She makes everyone around her better and always pushes her teammates to work harder and smarter."

Tamika hopes to see the WNBA stick around to offer many more generations of women opportunities to play. She's doing her best to build a fan base by being the best player she can be. "Every single time I step on the court I think of the one person in the audience who has never seen me play," she says. "I want them to go home and tell their friends. And I want them to see the best."

Watching Tamika on the court, they undoubtedly do.

What Are You Looking for Up There?

Lynn Hill

Rock Climber
Lynn Hill

First free climb of 5.14a The Nose in a single day 1994 (El Capitan, Yosemite National Park); first free climb of 5.14a The Nose 1993; winner of twenty-six out of thirty-eight climbing competitions entered (1986 to 1993); first woman to on-sight free-climb a 5.13b route, Simon 1992 (Frankenjura, Germany); first woman to free-climb a 5.14 route, Masse Critique 1990 (Cimaï, France); World Cup champion 1990; first free climb of 5.13d Running Man 1989 (Shawangunks, New York).

Opportunity hides in a granite face. The powder gray rock is mottled with blue, silver, black, and gold; its crystals are densely packed. Footholds and finger grips are small treasures uncovered through careful study. Legendary rock climber Lynn Hill knows this well. She runs her fingers over the shimmering face of El Capitan, the hulking bulwark of Yosemite Valley, on the most famous climbing route in the world.

It is 1993. She is 2,000 feet above the valley floor; only her fingertips and tips of her toes hold her to this granite wall. She slept last night on a ledge below this spot, a harness around her hips, oval-shaped carabiners securing her to the rock. Now she is steadily making her way upward, climbing the entire route—all 2,900 feet of it—by her own muscle. Far below, the Merced River curls into a lazy, lopsided S. Ponderosa pines, the giants of the forest, are little stalks of green from this vantage point. From down there in the valley, Lynn must appear as only a dark speck against the pale rock, a small shape almost imperceptibly inching upward.

The valley's native Indian tribe, the Ahwahneechee, named this rock Tutokanula, for an inchworm said to lead animals to safety down its face. And that's what Lynn is today, an inchworm, though she's inching her way skyward. Getting herself to move in that direction requires a complicated series of athletic maneuvers. Lynn uses her hands to walk up a narrow, vertical crack in the otherwise smooth rock. She pulls with her fingers and pushes with her feet, curling her back, creating vectors of opposing forces that will keep her pressed to the rock face. Above her, a lip of rock extends in a massive block that Lynn must climb from underneath. Called the Great Roof, this is the route's most difficult section. No climber, male or female, has ever successfully ascended this section without pulling on the rope in a technique called aid climbing. But Lynn's goal is to do this whole climb "free"—without using the rope to pull herself upward. She'll get no assistance; she's climbing every inch on her own.

Lynn is assembling a vertical puzzle. She shifts one hand before her foot moves right; the next hand moves up. She has climbed The Nose four times before, using aid techniques. Lynn knows this rock the way a violinist knows a beloved symphony; she is choreographing a dance, skyward, that is uniquely hers. This is what she loves about the sport of rock climbing—the challenge of adapting herself to the variations of a mountain, the creativity of building a path that suits her precisely, moving upward in a way no one has before.

"It's like learning a dance routine, or a gymnastics routine," says Lynn. "You practice the moves, you make it flowing and efficient. And eventually you do your performance."

Lynn Hill is not a tall woman. She stands under five feet two. She weighs not much more than a hundred pounds. Yet her short limbs take her to places no other climber can go. She's like a concert pianist who, though unable to span an octave, manages to move faster than anyone else across the keys.

Lynn clings to the face of El Capitan. At this point in her career, she has been ranked number one in women's rock climbing for most of the previous seven years. She has won twenty-six of thirty-eight competitions she's entered. She is widely regarded as the best woman climber of her generation.

And today, she'll carve her name into rock-climbing legend as one of the best climbers, period—male or female. With her free climb of El Capitan, she'll secure her position in the record books for all time, ascending into her reigning role as the queen of climbing.

Gray granite monsters delineate the curve of Yosemite Valley. Half Dome shimmers at its eastern end; to the west towers Cathedral Rocks and massive El Capitan, a boxy eagle head of a cliff. The rock is a soft gray that can turn an ethereal gold in early morning light. Its most prominent edge, the off-center beak of this giant bird, is The Nose.

Sixty-five million years ago, monster glaciers sculpted this beautiful landscape into being, fine artistry wrought from multiton blocks of ice. The cliffs are what make this place so beautiful. In the valley, "every rock seems to glow with life," wrote John Muir in 1894.

"The walls of these park valleys of the Yosemite kind are made up of rocks mountains in size, partly separated from each other by narrow gorges and side-cañons; and they are so sheer in front, and so compactly built together on a level floor, that, comprehensively seen, the parks they inclose look like immense halls or temples lighted from above," Muir wrote. "Some lean back in majestic repose; others, absolutely sheer or nearly so, for thousands of feet, advance their brows in thoughtful attitudes beyond their companions, giving welcome to storms and calms alike."

Families come to this place every summer to camp along the banks of the Merced River, to hike past willow trees and California poppies. They marvel at the spray of waterfalls cascading into the valley and exclaim when gusts of wind send the water frothing and misting into a giant bridal veil. And the children and parents, adventurers in retirement, RV travelers, and first-time campers all gaze up in wonder at these massive cliffs.

This valley has also drawn the world's most talented rock climbers. Lynn Hill first came here to climb when she was in her teens. Back then, in the late 1970s, the sport was hardly known beyond a few rugged circles. A descendant of Europe's mountaineering tradition and John Muir's poetic appreciation of the landscape, rock climbing in Yosemite, from the 1940s through the 1960s, developed out of the efforts of sport legends such as John Salathé, Royal Robbins, Yvon Chouinard, and Warren Harding. They brought varying outlooks to their approach; metalworker Salathé was an innovator in materials whose inventions helped Robbins and Chouinard develop free-climbing routes; the latter two, who sometimes climbed together, sought to minimize reliance on aid methods that required hammering bolts into the rock. Harding wanted to master the mountains. He was the first to climb El Capitan, in 1958; but it took him and his crew more than forty-five days of ascents and descents, and they used aggressive aid-climbing methods. To get themselves to the top, they hammered in a total of 125 bolts on the route.

The very first generation of Yosemite climbers included no women. A couple of decades later, when Lynn started climbing in Southern California, this had hardly changed. She grew up in Fullerton, in Orange County. In the 1970s, the area was a suburban Pleasantville, with rows of ranch houses fronted by two-car garages and sunny streets lined with palm trees. Her father was an aeronautical engineer, her mother a homemaker who worked as a dental hygienist after her youngest child was in daycare. The fifth child of seven, Lynn was a self-described tomboy and hunted for snakes around the neighborhood's black-edged tar pits, smaller versions of La Brea's dinosaur cemeteries. She liked to impress the other kids in the neighborhood by shimmying up the light pole.

"I don't even know where I got that idea," she says. "I didn't know about rock climbing. I just felt like climbing it."

Her first day out climbing, when she was fourteen, Lynn had no idea what she was getting into. Her oldest sister, Kathy, had been drawn into the sport by her boyfriend, Chuck Bludworth. They took Lynn to a place called Big Rock, near Riverside, a ninety-minute drive from home. Kathy told her to go up the rock. So Lynn tied into the long ropes and picked up the unfamiliar equipment—carabiners, pitons (small removable anchors), rubber-soled shoes called RDs—and climbed. She was nervous the first time she looked down at the ground, suddenly so far away, but it also gave her a surge of adrenaline. She set her focus on looking up and ahead. And the sport grabbed her. She liked using her muscles, strong from swimming and gymnastics, as well as her flexibility. She liked studying the rock face, finding the variation in texture that could make a path to the top. Figuring out how to put together a sequence of moves engaged her mind. And she was a natural. She impressed the group with her speed up that first route.

"By the end of the day, I knew I had been hooked on some new sensation," Lynn writes in her memoir, *Climbing Free: My Life in the Vertical World*. "I watched the late-afternoon sun turn the granite orange and highlight every nubbin and detail on its surface. Already I began to associate the beautiful form and texture of the rock with my desire to climb it. From that day on, I never saw a cliff in exactly the same way again."

Not long after her first climb at Big Rock, Lynn tackled a route rated 5.10+, the highest difficulty rating at the time. (Climbs now are rated from 5.0 to 5.15 and progress from 5.10 by letter grades a through d; for example, a 5.10b route is a bit more difficult than a 5.10a, and 5.11 is a step more difficult than 5.10d.) She was with Chuck Bludworth, her sister's boyfriend, who had fallen twice and exhausted himself attempting the climb. He suggested that Lynn try it. But she had no idea at the time what the difficulty rating meant. She remembers focusing intensely as she moved up this extremely challenging route. "The combination of controlling every position of my body and of forcing my mind to shut out the ever-present urge to submit to the very real fear of falling created an interesting result: a feeling that I was simultaneously acutely aware of both everything and nothing. Everything, because twenty-five years later I still recall the kaleidoscope of crystal patterns in the rock in front of me as I moved over it, and nothing, because at the time I was so immersed in the passage of movement that I felt no sense of time, gravity, or existence," she writes in *Climbing Free*.

Lynn began climbing as often as she could, heading out with her older brother Bob and Chuck. They traveled to Tahquitz and Suicide Rock, both near Idyllwild, and to what Lynn described as the "surreal landscape" of Joshua Tree National Park, where spiky palm trees and sagebrush fill the spaces between tortoise-shaped lumps of rock. She continued to compete in gymnastics and attend high school, but she says she thought about climbing all the time.

The summer after she graduated from high school, in 1979, Lynn headed to Yosemite to hone her skills with a group of serious climbers who spent all the time they could on the rocks, living at a now-famous campground called Camp 4. Photographs from the time show Lynn on a variety of challenging routes, her thick, honey-colored hair cut in layers, seventies style. Her climbing partners back then were also a shaggy-looking lot: John Long, John Bachar, Dean Fidelman, John Yablonsky, Ron Kauk, Mari Gingery, Jim Bridwell. They were mavericks, a group of oddballs and athletes who were drawn to testing themselves against the granite faces of the park. They scraped together enough to get by, living "on oatmeal and fifty cents a day," says John Long in the movie *Vertical Frontier: A History of the Art, Sport, and Philosophy of Rock Climbing in Yosemite.* But they all lived to climb. "We were just nonmaterial rebels," Lynn says.

In fact, the group included the best American climbers of the day. And the sport was about to take off, with a burst in popularity after the next decade's innovations in equipment and technique. Lynn climbed Half Dome, Mount Watkins, The Rostrum, and Sentinel Rock; she became good friends with the one other woman in the group, Mari Gingery. It was an incredible opportunity for Lynn, a case of the right athlete being in the right place at the right time. She studied the techniques of her climbing partners, picked up their styles—and impressed them all with her natural ability, building her own distinct style.

Evolved from mountaineering, rock climbing developed not just as a sport but also as a philosophy, an approach that harkens back to the exploratory spirit of Sir Edmund Hillary, Tenzing Norgay, and other alpinists who tackled Kilimanjaro, Nanga Parbat, and K2. A code of honor developed, more elaborate and philosophical than traditional sports' rule books. In traditional climbing, the style Lynn and her Yosemite partners practiced, if a climber fell, he or she was bound to descend to the route's beginning and start over. Climbers weren't to hang on the rope; bolts in the rock face—drilled or hammered in, sometimes secured with cement—weren't to hold a climber's weight, they were only there for safety. And all climbs were to start from the ground.

Traditional, or "trad," climbers did use aid-climbing techniques— but only out of necessity. Aid climbing has gotten people to places they would otherwise never have been able to get to. It includes using bolts and ropes to help climbers along. Aid climbers can "jumar" up a rope, using hand clamps that lock on to the strand to pull themselves up. They can hang on to the bolts to rest. In free-climbing, they can do none of these things—athletes still clip into bolts, using them simply for safety in case of a fall, but they don't rest on them at all; they don't use them to support weight. Free-climbing is the pure expression of trad philosophy, traditional climbing at its best.

It may sound like a fine distinction, but from the climbing point of view it makes an enormous difference in the effort required of the athlete. Aid climbing can still be very challenging, of course; but the spirit behind free-climbing is that the climber pulls herself up the rock face entirely on her own. Free-climbing tests how far a person can take herself on her own power.

For a while, Lynn juggled college classes in Fullerton with climbing, driving to Joshua Tree and Yosemite on the weekends. Soon, she and boyfriend John Long took off on an extended road trip through the western United States. It was a peripatetic existence; they moved from one western town to the next, filling in with classes and odd jobs where they could. They traveled to Phoenix to climb Granite Mountain. They climbed in Eldorado Canyon outside Boulder, Colorado, and at Independence Pass, near Aspen. They lived in Ophir, Colorado, near Telluride, and made first ascents on the difficult Ophir Wall. Here, Lynn became the first woman to lead a climb rated 5.13. They spent many months in Las Vegas. During this period, Lynn patched together a living, working at a furniture store, an Alpha Beta supermarket, a pizza place, and a diner, while Long took classes so he could get a job at a casino. Their goal was simply to have time to explore the little-traveled routes of Red Rock Canyon.

Lynn also relied heavily on winnings from an annual television show competition, *Survival of the Fittest*, a 1980s–style reality show that had competitors racing each other through obstacle courses, kayaking down rivers, rappelling down cliffs, and participating in foot races. The first place prize was $5,000 (later it was raised to $10,000 after Lynn protested when she discovered the men's purse was higher). Lynn competed against a top female jockey, a parachutist, several rock climbers, and a marathoner. She won her first competition in 1980 and placed first for the next four years.

In 1983, after Lynn and Long broke up, Lynn moved to the East Coast to try a new kind of rock. The region's best climbing is in the Catskill Mountains, outside the town of New Paltz, in an area called the Shawangunks. Here Lynn developed new skills, as the craggy quartzite rock was entirely different from the granite found in the West. Filled with overhangs and grooves, it required new rope-hanging arrangements, different approaches, and highly technical moves. Her first day climbing there, Lynn met a fellow climber and real estate salesman, Russ Raffa. They soon fell in love and were married in 1988.

Russ and Lynn were invited on a small group climbing tour of France in 1986. Lynn adored the soft, pocked limestone of Provence. It was yet another new landscape where she could pick up new skills. The limestone was well suited for the climbing competitions that were becoming popular in Europe. These were staged events on marked routes or sometimes artificial walls, where athletes went head-to-head on the same route on the same day. The events were drawing ever-larger crowds and prizes. Lynn was intrigued.

Climbers have always been a competitive bunch. But competing to be the first up a rock face is a diffuse battle waged over long distances against sometimes unknown rivals. This was something entirely new, but it was the kind of sporting event that could draw crowds and sponsors. Rock climbers were becoming celebrity athletes in France; this had yet to happen in the United States.

Lynn was invited to compete in France and excelled right away, winning most of the competitions she entered. She later became the first woman to ascend a 5.14 wall, at a route called Masse Critique in Buoux, France.

This was a time when a fissure was widening in the sport: A new approach called sport climbing was dividing athletes into two camps. Spurred in part by the growing number of competitions, the sport-climbing crew rejected some of the hallowed tenets of earlier climbers; instead of emphasizing the style and string of successive moves, sport climbing focused on trickiness and athleticism. It was a less humble, conquer-the-wall approach, harkening back in spirit to the macho hammering of Yosemite's Warren Harding. Sport climbers allowed themselves to rest on belay, hanging on the bolt-supported carabiners, in order to practice moves and investigate hold options. This became known as hang-dogging. The new approach also allowed climbers to descend from above a rock face in order to bolt a climb before attempting it from below, a technique labeled rap bolting.

Popularized by American climbers Tony Yaniro, Alan Watts, Christian Griffith, and Todd Skinner, sport-climbing techniques allowed climbers to scout out holds and practice moves while saving energy. It was a distinction similar to that between free-climbing and aid-climbing. But nearly everyone agreed that aid climbing was a lesser technique, one useful only when trad climbing was impossible. Sport climbers were insisting that their new approach was not only equal in achievement to trad climbing, but in fact a better way to climb.

Traditional climbers were outraged. This was anathema to their philosophies. In their eyes, the accomplishment of ascending a face was diminished if you rested in your harness or used rappelling to set up the most difficult moves.

In 1986, the American Alpine Club hosted a "Great Debate" over these two approaches. Trad climbers John Bachar, Ron Kauk, and Rob Robinson represented the old-school philosophy; Watts, Griffith, and Skinner the sport climbers. Lynn had grown up with trad climbing, and fellow climbers assumed she was in the trad camp. But Lynn had been climbing shortly beforehand in New York's Shawangunks, on a route called Vandals, rated 5.13a, and had been frustrated by the trad requirements of descending after every fall. By hanging on the route, she was able to eventually discover holds and finally to master it. This success expanded her view of sport climbing, she says.

"Even though I knew it wasn't necessarily acceptable style, it made a lot of sense to me," she said about hang-dogging shortly after her climb on Vandals. "It was a more enjoyable way of climbing."

During the debate, the mediator (a trial lawyer) criticized Lynn, implying she was hypocritical. Many present thought a climber had to be in one camp or the other. But Lynn believed there was a middle ground. Over time, this would prove to be true, and sport climbing and trad climbing coexist somewhat peacefully today. But at the time, this possibility seemed outrageous. Lynn was trying to straddle what others saw as an impossible divide. Yet it was typical: Lynn had made a career of getting herself into and out of impossible places.

After ranking number one in the women's field and competing in dozens of competitions, Lynn left the world of competitive climbing. She competed in her last World Cup in 1992 and participated in only a few international competitions in 1993. "I think when you're competing when you're young, it's about getting recognition. I didn't need that anymore. I wanted to learn more about the world. I didn't want to be stuck indoors," she says. "I started climbing way before there was competition. My motivation for climbing is different."

Lynn was making changes in her professional and her personal life. It was a transitional time. She and Raffa had grown apart, with Lynn's constant travel straining their relationship. They divorced in 1991. She bought a farmhouse in the south of France and decided to jump into what she loves best—free-climbing outdoors, learning french and later Italian, traveling to distant spots, and meeting people. She climbed in Cuba, Madagascar, Morocco, Vietnam, and Kyrgyzstan. "After competitions, I traveled around the world. It was much different than what I'd seen growing up in Southern California. I learned to speak different languages—that changes your brain and your thinking."

In 1989, while climbing in Provence, Lynn made a careless mistake. She let herself get distracted while attaching her rope to her harness. Instead of tying into the safety device, she left the rope tucked next to the straps as she walked to get her shoes. The rope was left, unknotted, as she started her climb. With her jacket covering her waist and the harness, her partner and others couldn't see this mistake. Lynn ascended seventy-two feet up the route, called Buffet Froid, on the Styx Wall, topped out, then leaned back to rappel downward. With nothing to hold it to her belt, the rope flew out of her harness. She fell back in the air, dropping as if from a seven-story building.

Fortunately, an oak tree partly broke her fall. She narrowly missed landing on one of the boulders that dotted the site. She bounced three feet when she fell, then slammed back into the ground face-first. She dislocated her elbow, fractured a bone in her foot, and required many stitches. She had two black eyes. But she was lucky to be alive.

"That's just miraculous that I didn't die," Lynn says. The accident prompted her to ask herself some big questions. "It's a wake-up call. It makes you focus on where you are in your life. It makes you ask, is there a purpose that my life has in this world? Everybody has their personal challenges—we all have our patterns of acting and dealing with people. I looked at all of those things for myself. If you don't do that you're missing out on a lot of growth. I think about things in a much more critical way now. And I'm still trying to resolve those things. It's a lifelong process."

Risk is an inherent part of rock climbing. The sport requires a lot of safety gear, but accidents happen, as Lynn's story shows, even to skilled professionals. Climbing and its sister sport of mountaineering have always appealed to push-the-limits personalities. And spending a lot of time in unstable terrain and frequent travel contribute to the danger factors.

Lynn is a cautious, rational climber. But she is familiar with tragedy. Many of her friends and climbing partners have suffered fatal accidents over the years. Her first partner, Chuck Bludworth, who became her sister's husband, died in 1980 on South America's twenty-two-thousand-foot Aconcagua peak. One of Lynn's most esteemed role models, the pioneering female climber Beverly Johnson, died in a helicopter crash in Nevada in 1994. A close climbing friend, John Yablonsky, a risk-taker who always lived on the edge, committed suicide in 1991. Another friend, a Frenchman named Hugues Beauzile, also perished on Aconcagua, in 1994. Dan Osmon, who was developing a bungee jumping–like sport he called rope flying, died in 1998 at Leaning Tower in Yosemite when his rope broke. Alex Lowe, a member with Lynn and Osmon of a North Face climbing team that journeyed to Kyrgyzstan together, died in an avalanche in Tibet in 1999.

Lynn is matter-of-fact when asked about the sport's hazards. "None of us are getting out of this world alive," she says wryly. Yet she has clearly done some soul-searching on the question of what draws her to rock climbing.

On a climbing trip to Vietnam in 1996, Lynn visited a fishing community on the Gulf of Tonkin. She and her partners had spent the day climbing the limestone cliffs above the water. A fisherman named Nguyen Mien stopped her to ask, "What are you looking for up there?"

Lynn was amused by his interpretation of their activity. "Nothing, really," she said, explaining the sport by likening its moving meditation to martial arts or tai chi. But the question stayed with her. What had she been looking for all these years? "Climbing is a form of exploration that inspires me to confront my own inner nature," she wrote after pondering the question. It allows her "to experience moments of true freedom and harmony."

Back on The Nose on El Capitan, on her record-blasting 1993 ascent, Lynn has herself wedged into the Great Roof's curl of granite, her head tucked under rock, fingers jammed into the cracks, feet pressed as firmly against the face. Her partner, Simon Nadin, tried earlier that morning to climb the face but was unsuccessful. He watches her from below, at the anchor at the base of the Great Roof. Lynn's rope is attached to him; he is attached to bolted pitons in the cliff.

Lynn moves her fingertips along the crack and her right foot slips off. She is surprised; her weight shifts; the rock slips away.

Nadin stops the rope in his hands. She swings into the curve of the roof and then falls, hanging by a purple thread. Pitons and other removable devices that Lynn has placed along her route catch the rope and stop her with a jerk. Her feet dangle, thousands of feet of air between them and the ground.

Lynn lowers back down to Nadin. She breathes heavily. "One more try. I'll do better next time," she tells him.

After twenty minutes of rest, she is ready to climb again. Lynn knows this is her last chance. The hot summer day has shifted into late afternoon. They have not moved far; the duo needs to get to Camp V, above their heads, before nightfall. If Lynn doesn't succeed now, they will have to abandon the goal to free-climb all of The Nose and resort to aid climbing to get to camp before dark.

Lynn lets her small fingers lead her up the seam in the rock for the third time today. She arrives at the Great Roof, where the seam veers to the right. Lynn follows it, wedging herself up under the heavy rock ceiling. Her arms are outstretched, fingers reaching into a crack that narrows to a quarter inch. She controls her center of balance, moves steadily along. She moves past the spot where she fell earlier.

Precision and control mark Lynn's style; she has been likened to a chess master while climbing. Her light blue eyes are intense. To climb well requires incredible strength and dexterity. Finger strength counts; toe flexibility matters. Lynn does not have the advantage of long limbs to reach holds at a distance, so she does what every great athlete does: She turns her vulnerabilities into strengths. Her small hands and fingers reach into spots larger athletes cannot grasp. Her natural flexibility helps her get her feet high to compensate for shorter arms.

Below the Great Roof, she is not far from this difficult stretch's finish. Only a few reaches are left on this sideways arc. Then her foot slips. She rolls backward. But she is curled up underneath the blue-gray ceiling; small and flexible, she is tucked up in a way few others could manage. She taps her head into the rock, catching her weight at her crown in a surprise save. She recovers, grasps the crack, and continues, reaching far to the right, her arm splayed. Using finger strength, she pulls herself sideways, then up, to a ledge.

As she has so often in the past, Lynn has used her head—this time literally—to get past a tricky spot on her record-setting climb. It's really her laserlike focus that has taken her to such incredible rocky heights. "Your mind is the thing that starts any movement. Your body follows. It's what's in your mind that determines where you go," Lynn says.

She is the first climber ever to accomplish what many had attempted: a free ascent of the Great Roof. Though she and Nadin won't finish the ascent of this route entirely free this time, she will return next week to free-climb the entire Nose route, making history in the process. The following year, she will free-climb the entire route, in less then twenty-four hours.

Living in Boulder, Colorado, Lynn today sees a broadening role for herself. She is extending her energy beyond rock climbing out to her community. "I've always been focused inward, too much that way," she says. "To do an activity like that so intensely makes you lopsided. Doing things I'm doing now, I'm more socially active. When I first started I was a climber—I didn't think about these things. Now as an adult, I'm more in a position where I feel a responsibility toward the community. I'm in the limelight. I have to make a statement about what I believe. That's what I can do."

Today, Lynn leads climbing camps, travels regularly, and goes climbing with her four-year-old son, Owen. She is an ambassador for the outdoor gear company Patagonia, founded in 1970 by climber Yvon Chouinard and known for promoting environmental causes. She has worked locally to clean up Boulder's drinking water.

She has found a balance. She recently free-climbed Leaning Tower in Yosemite, rated 5.13b, and she feels as strong as ever. "I climb better now. I have a more refined approach to it," she says. "It's subtle how your attitude, and the way you feel, can make a big difference on how you relax in a move or direct your force. There's the distraction of having your ego say, *I have to get there.* That thought keeps you from focusing on what you need to focus on. I just love to climb. If your motivation is so pure, if you just love to be there, you're not distracted. You're fully engaged."

Yet at this point she is not concerned about proving herself to others. "If you've been a champion, there are expectations from yourself and from others. There's a lot of pressure. But I'm not embarrassed to show whatever state I'm in at the time. I just go out there and join in the play with the community of climbers. I have one style of climbing, other people have different ones; we can all celebrate that. It's not about the winner of the game."

Of course, she is still pushing her own limits. "Just to be forty-five years old and do something better than I've ever done," she says. "That's what I like to do."

Acknowledgments

I'm enormously grateful to the athletes in this book—and their friends, family, and coaches—who generously took time to share their stories; thank you. Thanks also to sports agents Karen Linhart, Kimberly Moran, and Ray Flynn, the best and the classiest in the business; and to the staff at the invaluable Women's Sports Foundation in New York, particularly CEO Donna Lopiano, public policy coordinator Terri Lakowski, and ace researcher and superstar Yonit Caplow. Every athlete I spoke with credited her coaches for her success, and I understood entirely—thank you to writing coach Jill K. Jones, who was always ready with a pep talk or tough talk, depending. I want to thank my first tennis partner, my gram Ruth Silvian, who embodies grace in sport; my first coach, my dad Bill Taggart; and the glamorous Samantha Schoech, for appointing herself my life coach and taking the job so seriously. Thank you to Molly Watson, for agonizing with me when agonizing was necessary; to Sara Schneider, for always being on my side; to Richelle Dishno, for kindly listening to endless stories; and to Julie Chai, for her whirlwind of good ideas. Jim and Fran Gothers were generous with their car, their home, their barbecue, and the detailed driving directions required, thank you for this (and lots, lots more). Copy editor Donna Stonecipher improved the manuscript immensely; Tabitha Lahr did a great job with the design. A huge cheer of thanks to all-star editor Jill Rothenberg, for smart edits, too-often-tried patience, and for putting her considerable strength and endurance behind this project. Thank you also to pinch-hitter Laura Mazer, who gracefully stepped in and sent this home. And the Bottomless Coffee Cup Lifetime Achievement Award plus gratitude to the stratosphere goes to MVP Jimbo Gothers, for thoughtful editing, arcane sports smarts, late-night and early-morning latte runs, endless confidence bolstering, and—most important—for first showing me the inherent storytelling in sports that makes it all add up to more than just games.

For More Information

To follow **Jamilah Star's** quest to ride big waves, visit her website at www.femalesurfer.com. Catch the latest on the Women's Pipeline surf contest, held annually off the shores of Maui, at Betty Depolito's site, www.banzaibetty.com. Information about the Northern California big-wave contest at Mavericks can be found at www.maverickssurf .com. The documentary *Riding Giants* gives an excellent history of big-wave surfing (Sony Pictures, Stacy Peralta, dir., 2004).

Julie Krone's riding achievements are documented in Thoroughbred Racing's Hall of Fame in Saratoga Springs, New York; www.racingmuseum.org. Her memoir tells her story, from her childhood in Michigan through her recovery after her 1993 accident (*Riding for My Life*, Julie Krone with Nancy Ann Richardson, Little, Brown, 1995).

For information about **Julie Foudy's** sports and leadership camps for girls, visit www.juliefoudyleadership.com. You can learn more about the Bay Area Women's Sports Initiative and its programs with girls in California public schools at www.bawsi.org. Jere Longman's book *The Girls of Summer* gives a detailed, insightful account of the women on the 1999 U.S. soccer team and their journey to the World Cup (*The Girls of Summer: The U.S. Women's Soccer Team and How It Changed the World*, HarperCollins Perennial, 2001).

Follow race results and news on **Deena Kastor** at www.deenadrossin .com. More information about competitive running in general, as well as updates on Deena and her teammates, can be found at Team Running USA's site: www.runningusa.org. Progress in the global competition of elite runners through the World Marathon Majors is documented at www.worldmarathonmajors.com.

Wendy Hilliard's nonprofit gymnastics foundation is located in Harlem; www.wendyontheweb.org. She runs the gymnastics and youth sports program at Aviator Sports and Recreation in Brooklyn: www.aviatorsports.com. The AntiGravity acrobatic dance troupe will be performing in England in spring 2007; www.anti-gravity .com. Information about the current U.S. rhythmic gymnastics national team can be found at www.usa-gymnastics.org/rhythmic.

Misty May-Treanor's website is at www.mistymay.com. The national volleyball organization, the Association of Volleyball Professionals, has statistics, rankings, and match recaps, as well as current beach volleyball news: www.avp.com. The international organization Fédération Internationale de Volleyball includes information about indoor and beach competitions: www.fivb.org. The beach volleyball database has a wealth of game statistics: www.bvbinfo.com.

You can read more details about **Lynne Cox's** open-water swimming adventures in *Swimming to Antarctica: Tales of a Long-Distance Swimmer* (Harcourt Harvest, 2004). Her story of encountering a baby whale during a morning ocean workout is relayed in *Grayson* (Knopf, 2006). Lynne's website includes reading dates, interviews, and news about her latest projects: www.lynnecox.org.

Tamika Catchings has signed to play with the Indiana Fever through the 2007 season. You can read about her latest defensive moves, buy tickets, watch game videos, and analyze player statistics at www.wnba.com/fever. Information about Tamika's nonprofit Catch the Stars Foundation in Indianapolis, as well as regular notes from her journal, can be found at www.catchin24.com.

Karen Smyers trains with Team Psycho in Massachusetts; the team's website is www.teampsycho.com. News, races, rankings, and statistics about triathletes can be found at the website of the national governing body, USA Triathlon; www.usatriathlon.org. Track events leading up to the Hawaii Ironman and learn about past championships at www .ironman.com/worldchampionship.

Lynn Hill continues to lead climbing camps all over the world. Locations, dates, and registration information can be found at www.lynnhillclimbs.com. Hill's memoir (*Climbing Free: My Life in the Vertical World,* Lynn Hill with Greg Child, W.W. Norton, 2002) details her early start in the sport, her time in Yosemite—including her free ascents of The Nose—and her competitive career. A history of rock climbing in Yosemite, with footage from the sport's beginnings in the 1930s and '40s, is told in the film *Vertical Frontier: A History of the Art, Sport and Philosophy of Rock Climbing in Yosemite* (Kristi Denton Cohen/Peloton Productions, Kristi Denton Cohen, dir., 2002).

More on women in sports:
The Women's Sports Foundation has many resources online about professional women athletes, college sports, Title IX, and girls and teens in sports: www.womenssportsfoundation.org. A comprehensive, academic-leaning history of women's sports can be found in *Nike Is a Goddess: The History of Women in Sports* (Lissa Smith, ed., Atlantic Monthly Press, 1998). The photos and short essays in *Game Face: What Does a Female Athlete Look Like?,* the

companion book to the museum exhibit created by Jane Gottesman, cover a broad reach of modern sports history for women and are quite moving and inspiring (Random House, 2001); www .gamefaceonline.org.

Photo Credits

About the Author

A senior travel writer with *Sunset* magazine, Lisa Taggart is the coeditor, with Samantha Schoech, of two humor anthologies from Seal Press: *The Bigger the Better, the Tighter the Sweater: Beauty, Body Image, and Other Hazards of Being Female* and *Tied in Knots: Funny Stories from the Wedding Day.* She and her husband live near the soccer powerhouse of Santa Clara University in California. And she is mostly happy that writing this book ruined any possibility of her ever having a good excuse to skip a workout.

© JIM GOTHERS

Selected Titles from Seal Press

For more than thirty years, Seal Press has published groundbreaking books. By women. For women. Visit our website at www.sealpress.com.

The Nonrunner's Marathon Guide for Women by Dawn Dais. $14.95, 1-58005-205-4. A light and funny approach to women running marathons, complete with tips and strategies to making your training a success.

Women Who Run by Shanti Sosienski. $15.95, 1-58005-183-9. An inspirational and informative profiling of twenty very different women and what drives them to run.

Go Your Own Way edited by Faith Conlon, Ingrid Emerick & Christina Henry de Tessan. $15.95, 1-58005-199-6. An inspiring collection of essays by women who have traveled the world solo—on their own terms.

Zaatar Days, Henna Nights by Maliha Masood. $15.95, 1-58005-192-8. One woman finds spiritual rejuvenation on a journey from Cairo to Istanbul, with countless unforgettable detours along the way.

Incognito Street by Barbara Sjoholm. $15.95, 1-58005-172-3. From the founder of Seal Press comes this eloquent coming-of-age travel narrative about her beginnings as a writer.

Full Frontal Feminism by Jessica Valenti. $14.95, 1-58005-201-0. A sassy and in-your-face look at contemporary feminism.